LOVE YOU MORE

LOVE YOU MORE

The Harrowing Tale of Lies, Sex Addiction, & Double Cross

KERRY KERR MCAVOY, Ph.D.

Stones Roll

This book is my best recollection of what happened from 2016 to 2021. I have tried to recreate events, locales and conversations from my memories of them. To protect privacy, in some instances I have changed the names of individuals and places. I may have changed some identifying characteristics and minor details along with the chronology of a few events for a better reading experience.

To my three sons–Cameron, Devon, & Kellin

There isn't enough gratitude in the world to express my thanks for your unwavering support and faith.

You all are the joy of my life.

CONTENT

IN LOVE AGAIN

Three times love has breathed life in me.
It's heated my cold-stone body
Til it flowered bright and free.

The first two times, it didn't take.
The men's hearts slowly turned away,
And their love began to fade,
Causing my heart to throb and break.

My first husband chose fear.
He'd clutch his hands around his chest
And, from afar, try to hold me near.

Out of time, we hugged goodbye
As Death gave him a set of new eyes.
He still lingers to whisper and pray.
His fingerprints are on my sons' hearts today.

I fell in love a second time
With a monster playing a deadly game,
Wearing a mask
That hid his real name.

While Death took my first love,
It healed his wounded heart.
My second love was Death,
Wishing he, himself, could find a beating heart.

I'm in love again.
This time it's with life
And with all that could possibly be.
It's started deep within my heart,
And it has set me amazingly free.

—Kerry Kerr McAvoy, PhD

PROLOGUE

"Loyalty to that which does not work, or worse, to a person who is toxic, exploitive or destructive to you, is a form of insanity."
—Patrick J. Carnes, *The Betrayal Bond: Breaking Free of Exploitive Relationships*

I WAS TWELVE years old when Patty Hearst, granddaughter of newspaper publisher mogul William Randolph Hearst, announced that she had joined the Symbionese Liberation Army. Two months earlier, this same terrorist group had taken the nineteen-year-old hostage. Patty was later captured, convicted of bank robbery, and sentenced to thirty-five years in prison before being pardoned.

How could this young, well-educated woman walk away from what she'd known to join a violent group—the same one who had threatened her life and taken away her freedoms? Patty suffered from Stockholm Syndrome[1], which occurs when hostages develop a psychological bond

---

1. L. Lambert, "Stockholm syndrome." Encyclopedia Britannica. https://www.britannica.com/science/Stockholm-syndrome.

with their captors. Emotional manipulation uses fear to create an attachment, also known as a trauma or betrayal bond.

All of us are made for belonging. We are primed from birth to connect to our significant others and hardwired for self-preservation. In infancy, abandonment is our greatest fear since it spells death. We instinctually know we are at the mercy of our caregivers. Infants housed in an orphanage, even though well-cared for, if not touched and loved, are susceptible to infections. Their growth rate is stunted, and many will die. Abusers exploit this vulnerability by threatening the withdrawal of their love.

Through emotional manipulation, such as trauma bonding, the primal survival instinct is activated and used against the victim. Narcissists and other types of predators mirror their target's likes and dislikes. This kind of attunement is intoxicating since the targeted person has essentially met themselves. They think they've found their soulmate and quickly fall in love. But the initial lavish attention is deliberately withdrawn to create confusion. Victims unwittingly believe they're at fault and work to regain the love that has been lost.

Patrick Carnes, Founder of the Institute for Trauma and Addiction Professionals, writes, "Exploitive relationships create betrayal bonds. These occur when a victim bonds with someone who is destructive to him or her. Thus the hostage becomes the champion of the hostage taker, the incest victim covers for the parent, and the exploited employee fails to expose the wrongdoing of the boss." He further says, "These attachments cause you to distrust your own judgment, distort your own realities, and place yourself at even greater risk.[2]" In my work with women in mental health settings, I've seen them go to extreme lengths to save an abusive relationship. They often blame themselves for the problems and are willing to forgo self-respect and physical safety in the hopes of finally being loved.

2. Carnes, Patrick. Ph.D. The Betrayal Bond: Breaking Free of Exploitive Relationships (p. 20). Health Communications Inc. Kindle Edition.

A vulnerability to emotional coercion is unrelated to the mental strength of the victim, contrary to what some would like to think. It's estimated an abused woman makes an average of seven attempts before she's able to leave. This is not because she is weak; it's because she's been made to distrust what she sees, hears, and feels. She is no longer sure what is real. This can happen to any of us, including me, a psychologist.

Here's my story in which I became so confused, I nearly lost my way.

1

ESCAPE

"Love is blind, and a deaf-mute too."
—Patrick Rothfuss, *The Wise Man's Fear*

July 2016

I RUBBED THE sleep from my eyes and sighed. Another day.

Was it Tuesday or Wednesday? Since my husband Brad's death, they blurred into one another with the same blandness.

My ivory curtains billowed in the air-conditioning current. Sunlight peeked around the pleated blackout blinds.

My back complained; it was time to get out of bed. My friend Connie expected me at a nearby restaurant. I hesitated, reluctant. She had everything—a loving husband, two daughters she doted on, and an involved mother. I couldn't be the sister she never had or even the friend I used to be.

Life's unfairness had turned me bitter. These days I had to resist being nasty as she rattled on about her kids, and I resented seeing her kiss her husband goodbye. We once had never run out of things to say; now, there were long gaps of silence. Brad's passing had created an asymmetry—her life was full of what was missing from mine. Though we both pretended, our previous closeness was gone.

Losing Brad had changed everything. Widowhood had dislodged me from my previous social standing; now, I floated on the fringes as an outcast. The other women in my Bible study, all married, stumbled for the right thing to say. They would tilt their heads with sad smiles. "How are you?" they'd ask.

Not well.

I buried my head in the pillows as tears leaked. Dr. Hammitch had suggested at my last counseling session that I make a daily date with pain.

I stared, aghast. *I'm to hang out with pain?* But that evening, I did as she'd asked and sat in Brad's massage chair with the timer set for twenty minutes. At first, nothing happened and then an ache squeezed my ribs, and I heaved huge sobs. As the minutes passed, the pain diminished just as she'd said it would.

Brad and I met over summer break. Both in college, we had taken jobs at the same restaurant. Soon, we were inseparable. He was my first love, then husband and friend. We'd raised three sons. Though thirty-three years together had worn love a bit thin, I'd hoped we'd rekindle the passion once we had both retired. Then he was diagnosed with cancer.

On the wall above me several colored-triangle shapes danced. The stained-glass insert that hung in my window reflected the early morning sunlight. It had been a gift from Brad. Its weathered frame featured a bouquet of flowers cut from yellow glass surrounded by a multi-colored border; it most likely had once graced a historic home.

Brad must have heard me wish aloud for it. While emptying his socks drawer, I'd found a small white envelope. In his blocky penmanship, he had written, "For Kerry, Happy Birthday." Inside was a gift certificate for a local antique shop. He'd penned in the memo line, "for that stained-glassed window." I turned the card over and marveled at how he'd managed to purchase it.

Brad, who had been an engineer, wasn't the most imaginative guy. He liked to deal with concrete things, like numbers, sizes, and measurements, not things of the heart, but dying had softened him. He must have known he wouldn't live to see my next birthday and had found a way to surprise me. What our marriage lacked in intimacy, it had in loyalty. Brad had loved me with his whole heart.

When Brad died, my life imploded. Everything disappeared with him—the future, my job, and my partner. We would not be traveling across the United States, taking up golf together, or gazing at one another with astonishment as we held grandchildren. After losing him, I cried every day. Every. Single. Day.

"Go back to work," a friend said. I'd closed my small part-time counseling practice where for years, as a psychologist, I'd treated run-of-the-mill mental health issues. Most used therapy to address their latest relationship issues. I tried to imagine listening to the typical problems. How would I keep my envy in check? Offer a sympathetic ear to their lucky lives? I wasn't in shape to help others.

Brad's insurance meant money was no longer an issue if I was careful. Though his loss had set me free from the necessity of work, I didn't just lose a person but all the stability I'd once enjoyed—the love and acceptance I'd felt as a middle-aged woman. His death had left a gaping hole in my heart and my life.

I swallowed hard, trying to dislodge the lump in my throat, and pulled out my phone from beneath the pillow.

Among the notifications was the list of a dating service's latest matches. I'd signed up a few weeks after Brad had died. I knew it was much too soon, but I wanted what we had back, not someday but today.

To stave off the worst fears that I'd live the rest of my life alone, I kept a running list of the ideal man's qualities—all of Brad's attributes and more. Most people thought Brad and I had had a one-of-a-kind love. Given the way he'd died, I didn't challenge those assumptions. The truth was we had been slowly growing apart. Time, life's demands, and our priorities had eroded some of our previous closeness.

Maybe this time I'd meet someone even more compatible. Someone who could slide into the hole he'd left. This man needed to be someone with ambition, with a career he enjoyed. He needed to be sensitive, handsome, and a good dresser. Someone taller than me and in decent shape. He needed to be smart enough to talk about a wide range of topics. Someone with similar religious beliefs.

I threw myself into dating, desperate to find Prince Charming. Brad and I used to joke that he had a mistress—his job. Though I'd laugh, I'd sometimes secretly cry about it. Maybe this time I'd have a chance to find a different kind of love—all that I had had with Brad and more.

Some weeks I saw as many as three different guys—almost all single dates. One ended our meeting twenty minutes after it'd started. With the usual chitchat over, there was a long pause. My date swiped a strand of his salt and pepper hair out of his face, and our eyes locked. "What do you say to calling it a night?" He sat his half-drunk Manhattan cocktail onto the paper coaster while he waited.

This statement's startling directness left me no room.

"Okay," I replied.

He stood, signaled for the bill while pulling on his dark grey coat, then left. The abrupt dismissal was jarring. Though I'd come to the same conclusion, my chest felt like it'd been punched. The revolving door of men had left me jaded. I went from trying to be kind as I let them down to announcing at the end of the first meeting that I didn't care to see them again.

One of the last guys I met took me to his office for a quick look around. He'd asked if I'd be interested over a casual dinner of burgers. His open, vulnerable face made it impossible to say no.

My stomach sank as we pulled into the building next door to where Brad had worked for over twenty-five years. I pretended to be interested while he talked about his job. The proximity of Brad's empty office made concentration difficult. Everything within me ached for the familiarity Brad and I had once shared.

Brad's former office tugged like magnetic north on a compass needle when I pulled out of the building's garage. I used to wait for Brad after work, pregnant with our oldest son. I'd park in the small car lot next to his building and look up to see his silhouette in the office window. As I drove home after that date, I wept but refused to look back for fear I'd see Brad's specter.

All this effort was emotional work. I was exhausted.

When the dating service's subscription was ending, I knew it was time to quit. I needed to rest. But by the time I decided to take a break, I had missed canceling the automatic renewal by one day. I called customer service to complain, but they refused a refund. I could have afforded it, but growing up poor had taught me not to be wasteful. Determined to get the most out of the service, I perused the suggested men's profiles each morning.

Though I'd lost some of the weight I gained while caring for Brad, I wasn't slender. I referred to myself as curvy. I was pleasant-looking but not a beauty. A colleague had invited me to dinner. As we sipped the last of the wine, she announced, "You know, you'll probably have a hard time finding love again. You're too old, too smart, and too educated." I stared at her hard and added to the list, "too fat."

One of the latest matches caught my eye. His jet-black hair and youthful face popped like a neon light against the backdrop of graying, fifty-something professional men.

Curious, I opened his profile for a closer look. There were two photos of him, both taken at the same location. In the first, he was seated cross-legged and looking up. He stood against a bank of windows with a panoramic view of a city behind him in the second. There was something vulnerable about his smile. Maybe hopeful. It crinkled the corners of his eyes.

He'd dressed his tall, trim physique in slacks topped with a woven shirt. All he needed to complete the look was a suit coat slung over one shoulder. I lingered before swiping away. He was out of my league—a solid nine on the imaginary attractiveness scale to my optimistic six. The following morning, I awoke to a notification that he had visited my profile.

I opened the app. He was divorced, had two children, and worked in a managerial position. He'd listed five qualities titled "Deal Breakers" at the bottom of the page—no motorcyclists, tattoos or body piercing, atheists, liberals, or pet owners. He'd written, "I've realized I need to be more specific regarding the person I'm interested in after having some recent experiences. Please read my profile, and in particular this list, before contacting me."

I giggled. The odd disparity of items was arrogant but tame compared to the guys who wanted an attractive, much younger, slender woman. Curious, I sent him a brief introduction that mentioned a few things we shared in common and asked if he'd be interested in getting to know me.

By day's end, he messaged back, "I'd like that."

I smiled to myself, flattered.

And just like that, our relationship began.

2

CAPTIVATED

"I see no evil 'cause love is blind."
—Ljupka Cvetanova, T*he New Land*

Early August 2016

IAWOKE AND shot a look at the alarm. *Shit!* I bolted for the shower. After throwing on some makeup and dressing in beach shorts and a tank top, I grabbed the picnic basket and ran for the door.

Two weeks ago, Cesar suggested he fly in for a quick overnight.

"Really?" I asked. "You'd travel for a visit?" Most men were reluctant to meet for coffee.

"It's just an hour by air." He laughed. "I'll stay at a hotel near the airport."

I exhaled with relief. "Sounds good."

At the first stoplight, I heard the sound of an incoming text. "I'm here!" he wrote.

With one eye on the road, I typed, "I'm on my way!" and fumbled to hit send.

A few minutes later, the phone rang. It was Cesar. I answered and saw a blinking cursor beside the unsent text. *Crap.* "Hi, it's me!"

"Did you get my message? I'm standing outside of the airport." His voice sounded curt. He added, "No rush, though. I just wanted to let you know the plane landed early." His chuckle dispelled the tension.

"I thought I replied, but it didn't get sent. Sorry about that. I'm only a few minutes away."

"I was getting nervous when you didn't show."

"No worries, I'm almost there!" My pulse raced. Was I ready to meet a stranger? What if we didn't hit it off? I let out a long breath.

Once in the airport's arrival area, I slowed to a crawl. A tall, dark-haired man, holding a small brown suitcase, stood out among the few loiterers. In his short-sleeved shirt and shorts, he appeared thinner than in his photos. I waved before pulling over. With my heart in my mouth, I stepped out.

"So nice to meet you!" With a big grin, Cesar stuck out his hand. For a moment, my icy-cold palm warmed in his grip.

"Yeah, you too." I stumbled for the next thing to say. My cheeks flushed. Cesar loaded his luggage in the trunk and took the passenger seat beside me. Despite being my guest, he had won the imaginary coin toss for control with his confidence.

He was larger than life. His booming voice and waving hands breached the car's quiet sanctuary. I winced. All people did this to me on the first encounter; it didn't matter if they were strangers or family. I described it as warming up slowly, part of my introverted nature.

Cesar's boisterousness was the first thing I noticed. He smiled often. It was the kind that lit his face and scrunched his eyes like a jack-o'-lantern. He shared about his kids and work, providing just enough detail to keep it interesting. Slowly any lingering fears were quelled as the miles passed, and my shoulders relaxed.

Despite it being another hot day, only a few cars were scattered about the beach's parking lot. I looked over at him, momentarily awkward, as though to say, *"This is it. Our date begins."* Exhaling, I hit the trunk fob. "Let's find a spot close to the water." My stomach flip-flopped between excitement and nervousness.

"Sounds good."

Cesar began to unload the heavy items, slinging them over his shoulders until he stood hunched. Only a small cooler and a tote bag remained.

I reached out to take something. "Here, let me help you."

"No, it's okay. I got it." He made a faltering step forward. "It's time for someone to take care of you."

I smiled awkwardly. "Okay." Receiving help was something foreign. On the childhood family farm, everyone had been expected to do chores. Brad would chafe if he thought I wasn't doing my fair share.

I trailed behind on the downhill walk. Warm sand seeped through the crevices of my slip-ons and pooled in the back of the heels, making each step heavier than the last. My empty arms felt oddly useless.

"Is this spot good?" Cesar paused a few yards from the edge of the lake. The water lapped against the shore in a quiet rhythm. A few boats with white sails dotted the horizon.

"It's perfect!"

I unfurled a large towel. Cesar grabbed the loose end that billowed in the wind. He opened the beach chairs while I anchored the umbrella to the ground.

Another wave of shyness dried my mouth as we sat down. The day stretched ahead with its too many hours. I opened two wine coolers.

"Cheers." Cesar tipped his bottle in my direction. The everydayness of this gesture had a calming effect.

"Cheers."

We leaned back; the silence thickened. I took another sip and peeked at him. Our eyes met. The smell of his cologne was musky. *Is his hair soft or wiry?* I wondered.

He stared out across the water. "This is nice."

I followed his line of sight. "Yeah, it's one of my favorite places." The tension eased. "I hoped you'd like it."

"I do." Cesar stretched out his long, dark legs. They were slender but muscular. Powerful. My eyes traveled upwards. His mouth was generous with full lips, and his eyes a warm chocolate brown. Desire stirred in my lower abdomen.

Cesar took a swig as if drawing courage. Straightening, he tugged at the bottom of his shirt. "Let me tell you a bit about myself."

I became alert.

"I was born in Mexico and moved to the US in my early twenties. Later, I finished college. I have two kids; both are grown and doing well." He smiled proudly. "I'm a manager at a large company," he said. "And I love it."

I smiled encouragingly.

He exhaled with a quick smile. "What about you?"

I swallowed. "Well, I've shared most of this before. As you know, I'm semi-retired and write now—mostly from home. I have three sons. One of them, Devon, has been living with me since his dad died."

"How's that going?"

"Being a widow or sharing a condo with my kid?"

He gave a laugh. "Both, I guess. I've been doing some research on dating a widow."

My mouth fell open. *He'd been looking into dating someone like me?* "Well, it's been a big change. But, overall, it's okay."

"Do you plan to go back to work?"

"Counseling?"

"Yeah."

"Nah." I shook my head.

He stared in disbelief. "Why not?"

I hesitated. Early in my marriage to Brad, we'd decided to live debt-free. While others took lavish vacations, we stayed close to home. We bought used cars instead of new ones and stuck to a budget. And then there was Brad's life insurance.

"Because I don't need to." My ears buzzed, fearing I'd said too much.

He nodded.

Most dates tended to dominate the conversation. They would ask a few questions but act bored when I responded. Cesar's attention was different. Genuine.

I checked my watch; it was noon. "You hungry?"

"Lunch sounds good!"

"Great. I brought stuff for sandwiches." As I pulled food from the cooler, I noticed that the meat, tomatoes, and dressing were missing. "Oh, no!"

"What's wrong?"

"I forgot some of the food!" I pawed through the contents again. "I can drive to the local sub shop." I looked around, trying to think of another solution.

"No, it's okay," Cesar said. "I'm all right. What's here is fine." He patted my arm.

My neck burned while we ate the remaining food in awkward silence.

"I have something to tell you," Cesar said softly. "I waited until we met."

I stiffened for an imaginary blow.

With his eyes trained on some distant point, his cheeks reddened. "I've been married four times." The admission hung in the air. "It's not something I'm proud of, but it's something I think you should know."

Blood roared in my head. *Four marriages! I knew this was too good to be true.* "What happened?"

"I looked for the wrong things, but each ended for a different reason. With the first one, I wanted out of my parents' home more than I loved her. The second was my longest, but it was riddled with fights; the third valued her friendships more than me, and the fourth lied about her legal history," he said. "It's hard to trust someone after something like that."

What he said made sense, yet his rationale left me uneasy.

Still looking straight ahead, he continued, "My mother asked why I wasn't interviewing prospective dates the same way I would a possible employee. So, this is new—thinking of a date like an interview." He gave a quick smile. "I've asked myself what qualifications I want in the next wife." For a moment, listening to him, I wondered if I would qualify for the part. "I'm looking for—a friend, a wife, a lover, and a girlfriend." He ticked a finger off with each one.

"That's a good list..." I started, surprised by its shallowness, but said nothing further. *Most dates put themselves in a favorable light by glossing over the unflattering parts,* I reminded myself. Confrontation came hard, though I had to do it as part of my counseling job. I survived a crazy childhood by being easy-going.

He relaxed as though the worst was over. "I grew up in an abusive home," he said. "My dad would beat us. It'd get bad after he had a few drinks."

Cesar's cultured mannerisms and grooming hid a troubled background well. Were these disclosures a show of trust?

"Holidays were the worst." His eyes met mine. "I hate Christmas."

"My dad did too," I said. "His stepfather was an alcoholic, but he rarely spoke about it." I hoped that sounded supportive rather than competitive.

"I don't like to talk about it either. But since you are a psychologist, I figured you'd get it." He looked down. "It's one of the things that attracted me to you." He glanced up; his face flushed.

"Thanks for telling me." No one I'd met had gone this deep, this fast.

He let out a long exhale. "I was sexually abused."

Goosebumps rose across my body.

"I didn't see it as abuse," he said. "I thought I was lucky to have an experienced older woman teach me sex. It wasn't until a few years ago that I learned differently." He paused. "Right in the middle of some workplace training, it hit me; I'd been molested." He shook his head. "I had a panic attack and had to leave."

A strong urge to hug him came over me. "I'm so sorry." *Should I tell him about my abuse?* My heart sped up. Some had concluded after hearing about it that I would have sexual problems. Yet, not disclosing it might appear secretive. "I was sexually abused too. By my teenage uncle." I blew out a long breath.

"So, you understand." This sounded more like a comment than a question.

"Yeah, I do."

A look passed between us.

"Well, this got heavy." He laughed nervously. "I feel better, a lot better now that's all out of the way!" His gaze softened. "I knew you would understand."

"I do." I returned his smile, though unsure if I'd been ready to share these things. There was a kinship here. A strong compatibility. We were near the same stage of life, had similar experiences, and shared spiritual belief. Our kids were near the same age. But I needed to ask a question. My deal-breaker.

I blurted out, "Are you into porn?"

My mind flashed to the pages of the men's magazine my mother had shown me years earlier. I must have been in middle school. That was back when my dad was farming. Tough years with long hours in the fields tending the crops and in the barn milking cows.

My mom said she'd found these few pages in the cornfield behind the dairy barn. They must have been blown out of some neighbors' trash bin and got caught among the bent corn stalks.

Our breath hung in the air on that cold winter morning as she smoothed the wrinkled pages flat against the top of the massive steel tank where we stored that day's milk for pickup.

"See? See how the women pose themselves with their legs apart? Such immodesty." Her lips curled into a sneer as she pointed at the ladies' splayed bodies. She snorted in disgust.

Shock rocketed through me. I'd never seen female sex organs before. I'd read how to use a mirror to view mine but had been too scared to try. These women looked wanton, taunting, and shameless with the red gash of their genitalia exposed.

My tongue stuck to the roof of my mouth, and my feet melted into the concrete floor. Silent and frozen.

With my mother's gaze locked onto the pictures, she hadn't noticed my distress, so caught up with what she'd found.

"This is the stuff some men like. I wanted you to be aware so that you're informed." She exhaled a long breath. "Such garbage."

I was ashamed of my association with the gender. Good girls don't act this way. They don't want sex like this.

She wadded up the pages to be thrown away, not realizing my sexuality had gotten caught among them to be discarded, too.

Time suspended as I waited for Cesar's reaction.

He gave me a direct look. "No," he said in a firm voice. Was there something he wasn't saying? He'd been open about his family and the sexual abuse. I let the subject go.

The sun hung low in the sky as we packed. By the time I dropped Cesar off at the hotel's entrance, I was exhausted. I started to get out when he stopped me.

"Stay in the car. It's been a long day." He leaned over to kiss my cheek.

On the drive home my mind raced. Did I really want to get into a relationship with someone who had been married four times? Had he learned from his mistakes? Figuring there were no straightforward answers, I collapsed into bed.

The next morning I awoke feeling hungover, fatigued from the previous long day. I canceled our plans to visit church but offered to take him to the airport.

Once in the hotel's lobby, I texted that I'd arrived. At the sight of Cesar, my breath caught in my throat. His black slacks and white-collared shirt offered a sharp contrast to his still damp jet-black hair.

"Do you mind waiting in the room while I finish packing?" he asked. His smile made his eyes dance. I gulped hesitantly. I considered telling him I'd preferred to wait where I was but instead followed.

The king-sized bed loomed. I sat on the opposite side as far away as possible. Cesar moved about, folding his clothes, comfortable in his body. Confident.

The air crackled between us as we chatted. Would he find an overweight, middle-aged woman attractive? Especially one who suffered from alopecia and wore a wig? I never knew when it was the right time to tell a new date that I had lost most of my hair after the birth of my last child. The number of people who knew could be counted on two hands.

Cesar put down a handful of folded clothes. Our eyes met as he walked towards me. He lingered for a second. His breath warmed my face, and his cologne scented the air. Our lips touched; his mouth was soft.

He ground his hips into mine, his presence suddenly overwhelming. I forced myself to hold still and focused on my breathing instead. He stepped back. "I'm surprised I want you so much." His voice was husky. I shrugged off this odd admission, figuring I'd misheard him.

He directed us towards the bed once more—too close, but also exciting. With a trail of kisses, he unbuttoned my jeans and parted my legs to stroke me with his tongue. It had been so long. *Do I want this? No... yes...* The inner turmoil quieted. Cesar watched my face as I threw my head back and climaxed. He looked pleased.

While I pulled on my jeans, red-faced, he grabbed the last of his things. "Let's do this again," he said. "In two weeks?" He smiled shyly. With my head hung, I nodded.

A few minutes later, we arrived at the airport. Cesar gave a quick half-wave goodbye before the terminal doors closed behind him.

3

NECESSARY SACRIFICES

"We accept the love we think we deserve."
—Stephen Chbosky, *The Perks of Being a Wallflower*

Mid-August 2016

I STOOD UP, smoothing the creases from my pale blue pants, and waited to disembark the plane. I'd dressed special as this was my second weekend with Cesar. I tapped my foot and huffed as the line of people ahead of me inched forward.

Two weeks earlier, Cesar and I'd met for the first time. Each day since, we'd texted and called. He'd given me a new pet name, "Gorgeous." No man had called me by another name since my father.

"Are you my Skeeter?" my dad would ask. He'd sip his cooling coffee and sigh wearily. He sat at the kitchen table, still in his dusty coveralls.

Giggling, I'd swing back and forth from his chair rung. "Skeeter?" I'd say. "Why that name?" I'd beam while I waited for him to give the same answer I'd heard before.

"Cuz you're like a mosquito, always *buzz-bombing* around." He'd softly chuckle.

As I watched the line of people exit, I thought, *I'm in love. Am I ready to have sex?* The last time Cesar and I met, oral sex had happened, but in my mind, that didn't count. This weekend would be different. The church preached sex outside of marriage was wrong, but I wasn't on good speaking terms with God.

My therapist would approve the sex part but would say it was too early for love. "There's no need to rush."

I snorted. That's easy for her to say. On social media, she'd posed next to a man, leaning against his shoulder, with their arms linked. As they faced the camera, their broad smiles stretched ear-to-ear. Her seemingly rich love life accentuated the emptiness of my own.

I was tribe-less. Most people, my therapist included, wouldn't believe this. "You have people. Look at all of the comments on your social accounts," they'd say. But public likes or follows couldn't hold me at night or talk me out of a panic. These days my sons rarely called, and most of my friends had backed away now that our shared commonality of being married was gone.

Last night, in anticipation of spending the weekend together, I texted to warn Cesar about my wig.

"I noticed there was something different about you in your photos. Have you been sick, Gorgeous?"

With trembling fingers, I typed, "No, no, nothing like that. I just wanted you to know I'll be wearing a nightcap."Brad disliked discussing my baldness. He'd squirm. "You look beautiful. That's all that matters," he'd say before changing the subject. For a long time, I'd dreamed of being found out. A woman's beauty was her hair. Letting Cesar see me bald was out of the question.

I twisted the corner of the duvet into a tight knot while I waited. A notification appeared of an incoming email. Taking a deep breath, I opened it.

"Sweetie, I'm tired of playing games. We need to be honest about everything—even our appearance. Unless you can be open with me, I don't think I can move forward."

"What?" My eyes flew wide. *Be open with him? Go bareheaded? He must not understand what he's asking; I can't even stomach looking at myself.* Gulping for air, I dialed his number. "What's the meaning of this?" Tears burned.

There was a long pause. "I think the letter says it best."

"We're off if I don't let you see me without a wig or a nightcap?" I could barely speak these words.

He exhaled. "I'm too tired to pursue a relationship if it isn't real. You'll have to decide if you're up for this level of honesty."

"I don't know what to say." Tears dripped.

"Only you can decide if this is what you want," he said wearily as he ended the call.

Hadn't this been the kind of vulnerability I'd been longing for? I sobbed harder.

The people in the seats ahead of me exited. I moved into the aisle. *True love was sacrificial. It took risks.* If my feelings for Cesar were sincere, then his expectation of vulnerability was understandable.

Though my marriage to Brad had been good, self-disclosure hadn't come easy. Both of us had been raised in troubled homes. In Brad's, conversations were rare except for his father's jeers or the siblings' fights. Family dinners were silent affairs except for requests for a dish to be passed. Brad disliked intimate discussions. Whenever a touchy subject would come up, he'd squeeze his eyes shut. "Can we talk about something else? This reminds me of therapy," he'd say as though that were a bad thing.

The airport hummed with activity. A line of passengers waiting to board the next plane stretched across the corridor like a long tail. I headed to baggage claim. The world looked new. Fresh.

I saw a sea of luscious red roses as I exited the escalator. Each velvety-red bud sat perched on a long stem, trimmed, with a few dark olive leaves. Their scent perfumed the air.

Cesar shuffled forward with his head hung. "Here, these are for you." He pushed them into my arms.

"They're lovely!" I gasped.

The drive to the hotel was quiet; I stole glances at Cesar. Once alone, he intertwined his fingers through mine to pull me close. We slowly danced, our bodies gently rocking while he sang, *"Bésame, bésame mucho..."* His voice quivered off-key.

I leaned my head against his warm shoulder, and the sting of last night's disagreement disappeared. "I love you," I heard myself say.

He drew back. A slow smile spread across his face.

"It's okay if you're not ready to say it!" I blushed.

Still grinning, he drew close to kiss me. His soft lips became insistent. He tugged us in the direction of the bed.

"I need to do something first," I said.

A wrinkle appeared on his forehead.

"It'll just take a second. Wait for me, okay?"

Once alone in the bathroom, I scrutinized my face. There were no signs that I'd spent the night crying. With a big breath, I tugged the hairpiece off. In the mirror, a stranger looked back. A pariah. Someone hideous.

"You can do this." I stood a bit taller.

Cesar lay naked. The sheet draped across his upper thighs hid nothing. "Come over here," he said.

Heat crawled up my neck as I scurried beside him and buried my head beneath the fluffy covers.

Cesar drew close. My heart pounded as I watched him for a reaction. No one, outside my hairdresser, had seen me like this. He kissed the top of my thinning hair. His gaze was soft, and he smiled gently. His arousal acted as a sign of his acceptance. I exhaled slowly and pulled him into my outstretched arms and parted legs.

Cesar tried to push himself in. It had been a while since I'd last had sex; the fit was tight. Heat crept up my neck. I considered asking to be touched, but the words stuck in my throat. Cesar thrust a few times, then gave a look of frustration. He knelt to change the angle, but his soft cock curled. He pulled me across the bed. I helped by scooting, conscious of my weight.

"Relax. Let me do this." With a huff, he patted my thigh. This was said matter-of-factly like the act of sex was the point. I stared in surprise. *Where were the words of love?*

He tried to enter again.

My butt slipped off the bed. "I'm falling!"

"No, you're not. I got you," he said. "Just relax, okay?"

I slid further.

He wrinkled his forehead. "Just relax." He shook my legs. "Okay, get back on the bed."

I finished dropping to the floor. With burning cheeks, I climbed back on the mattress and crawled to the center. Everything about this felt strange. The thirty years of sex had taught me what Brad liked. But Cesar wasn't Brad, and I'd become an awkward virgin.

He tried to penetrate, his arousal gone. After several attempts, he entered. "Someone's tight." He chuckled.

No, that's not the problem. Embarrassed for him, I pushed the thought away. "It's been a while."

"You're as tight as a virgin. My virgin, Kerry." He gave my derriere a quick slap. I grimaced.

Cesar's erection stiffened. I winced in time to his rhythm, hoping this would soon be over.

Finally, he dropped beside me, sweaty and panting. "How was it?" he asked, full of smiles. But before I could answer, he added, "Nice ass. I was a little worried until I saw it."

My eyes bulged. "Well, that's good." I smiled weakly.

After a quick kiss to my forehead, he fell asleep. My mind turned while I stared unblinkingly up at the ceiling. It had been so long since I'd been loved. Was that what this was? *It'll get better. Just wait and see.*

My sex life with Brad had stuck to the center lane. We avoided anything that would make us blush. While that part of our marriage may not have been imaginative, it offered an intimate sweetness that daily life often lacked.

My favorite day of the week was Saturday. Most mornings we'd dawdle in bed. After dreaming of the future and reminiscing about the past, we'd make love. Cancer had snatched that away. The first few weeks Brad was sick, he spent most days trying to keep food down, and for the next several months, he recovered from a surgery that had split his gut wide open. As his body healed, his mind didn't. Cancer erased tiny pieces of who he once had been. Sex got lost like a child's toy that had rolled under a piece of furniture—mentally forgotten after having gone missing. A cancer patient's wife was supposed to be superhuman—above such things, like missing sex. But I did—something fierce.

A friend had recommended a vibrator. Sweating nervously, I perused the online options of phallic-looking ones until I'd found something nondescript—a large wand with a thick bulb at one end, more of an appliance than a toy.

Brad had just parked in the garage, one of his last times behind the wheel when I brought the subject up.

"Uhhh..." I said, floundering for the right words. My face grew hot. "I purchased something. Something I thought might help our sex life." I could feel the weight of his stare. "A vibrator." I finally met his eyes.

"Why would you do that?" He sounded defensive.

"Because I miss you. You're tired and sick..." I trailed off. "I thought this would help."

"I can't believe this," he bellowed.

"I thought you'd like the idea." I began to cry.

"Like it? Why would I like it?" he said. "You should have talked to me first."

"I know, I should have. I'm sorry," I said, dropping my head.

"I'm afraid you'll prefer it to me," he muttered to himself.

Prefer a vibrator to you? We aren't even having sex. I peeked at him but held my tongue. Brad was staring off, his mouth pinched tight.

A few nights later, he brought up the subject. "Want to try that thing?"

"You sure?" I gave him a long look before pulling the large wand from its hiding spot. This no longer seemed a good idea. The apparatus buzzed. Staring at a nearby wall, he touched my crotch in a wide circle. A pleasant sensation would begin, then disappear.

After several minutes, I whispered, "No worries, I'm fine."

"Okay." And he let it fall to the floor.

I waited until he slept to cry. Intimacy had been discarded months before he died. I missed it terribly but didn't dare complain. I was the lucky one who would get to live.

How did God feel about what I'd done today? After a lifetime of trying to do the right thing, I was no longer sure who God was or how the spiritual rules worked. Would he approve? Probably not, but I was too angry to care.

The hotel's air conditioning tickled a few strands of my hair. I moved to get out of bed.

"No, don't." Cesar tightened his grip.

"I need to use the toilet." A half-truth I hoped would work.

"Not yet," he pleaded.

I lay still, feeling exposed.

"Okay... you can go."

Mistaking his need for control as desire, I scooted away with a pleased smile. Alone again, I clipped on the wig. I bent close to the mirror and scrutinized my image. I looked vulnerable but happy.

Cesar was awake and sitting upright when I returned. He glanced up from watching TV. "You put your hair back on. You don't need to do that," he said. I pulled it free; the room's air chilled my naked scalp. After slipping his arm around me, he kissed my head, softening the request. His bare chest was warm. I dozed to the sound of the droning voices on the television.

The following day, we packed. My flight didn't depart for several hours. For years, Sunday brunch had been a family tradition. I'd planned to suggest Cesar and I do the same. He walked out of the bathroom dressed in football fan attire. Team-colored beads hung around his neck.

"Hey, you'd be okay if I dropped you off at the airport early? I forgot to mention my son and I are going to a game," he said. "You wouldn't mind, right?"

"What?" I replied.

"That'd be okay, right?" He waited.

"What?" I stared blankly.

"It'd be just a few extra hours at the airport." He shrugged as though this request was small.

When I'd booked the flights, I called to discuss departure times. This had never come up. With a cool voice, I answered, "Okay." *Stupid, stupid! I should have been clearer.*

Cesar filled the awkward silence with talk of sports trivia on the trip to the airport. I half-listened as I watched the cars pass. *This is my fault. I should have communicated better.*

With the last of my luggage sitting on the sidewalk outside of the terminal, he stopped in front of me. With his head down, he held out a large, clear plastic bag filled with rosebuds. "Here are the flowers. I thought you could dry them so we'd have a reminder of this weekend," he said.

"Ohhh, thank you!" A warmth of surprise rose over me.

He squeezed me close to whisper in my ear. "I love you, Gorgeous."

With those words, my anger melted away. "I love you too."

As I traveled home, I watched the clouds drift past the jet window. The scratchiness of the wig's dry hair across my neck reminded me of the weekend.

"Would you like something to drink?" the flight attendant asked.

Startled, I glanced into the stiff smiling face of a young woman. Her starched uniform matched her rigid stance. "Yeah... um... diet cola, please?"

After a sharp pop of a pull-tab, she handed me a small plastic cup filled with ice and a can of soda followed by a napkin. With a quick nod, she moved on.

All relationships required some type of compromise—the size of the bargain depended on the person. Some wanted something small, others something big.

I had lost a bit of integrity to Brad. He'd pushed for sex too soon, though not on the first date, like Cesar. I'd been an inexperienced virgin.

It had happened shortly after we'd started hanging out. With his morning shift done, he had stopped by my studio apartment. My roommate had left hours earlier, leaving us alone.

At first there were long pauses between snippets of chitchat. Brad leaned for a kiss. Our lips touched, then the kiss deepened as he opened his mouth. He stretched his body across mine. I could feel his penis, hard and ready. It had bunched his jeans. He tugged at the fabric before grinding his hips into mine. I said nothing, choked with fear. The farthest I'd gone was making out with a guy in the college lounge under the watchful eye of the dorm monitor.

Brad moaned. Sweat coated his forehead. "I want you," he groaned. "Oh?" I said, hoping my scared voice sounded warm.

His thrusting became insistent, and he panted faster. Then he suddenly rolled upward as if to pause like a cat in a mid-arch stretch. He puffed several long breaths into my face like a train engine releasing steam.

I stared. *Did he just cum?*

He rolled off and wiped his brow. With a broad smile, he fell beside me. "Can I do you?" he asked.

For a moment, tongue-tied, I said nothing. *Does he mean touch me down there?* "No, I'm good."

He snuggled close to doze.

Had I wanted this? I wasn't sure. While I listened to the soft sound of his breathing, I focused on the sensation of being desired. It reminded me of being tucked in all warm and cozy under a heavy quilt on a cold winter's night. *Had it been worth my sexual integrity?* That question no longer mattered.

Cesar had pushed sexual boundaries too, and once those lines had been breached, they were hard to protect. Did it matter that Cesar's insistence I go without my wig cost me self-respect?

All working relationships require some concessions, I repeated to myself. With a glance out the window, I thought, *Yes, I can live with this one.*

Once back home, I met Connie for breakfast.

"So, how was he?" she asked. I gazed at her expectant grin and gulped, wishing I'd never told her about how great the first date had gone. She waited, her eyes shining.

How was he? That was too complicated of a question.

"Fine. It was good," I lied.

4

HAPPY

"To burn with desire and keep quiet about it is the greatest punishment we can bring on ourselves."
—Federico García Lorca, *Blood Wedding and Yerma*

September 2016

OVER THE NEXT several weeks, Cesar showed different sides of himself. He was gentle, even protective. Kind and sweet. Both my father and Brad, though loyal, had been preoccupied with work. Women were to toil alongside them yet have a hot plate of food ready when it came time to eat.

Cesar was different. During a rare local tornado warning, he called. "Are you okay?" His voice was high-pitched with fear.

"Yeah, yeah. Devon and I are moving to the basement now."

"Okay, okay. That's good to hear." He paused, then whispered, "I had the strongest urge to start driving towards you." He gulped. "Then I realized I'd never get there in time."

Each visit, he would rave about what he'd planned; his face glowed, lit from within. We wandered Millennial Park in downtown Chicago, visited the Mall of America's Aquarium, and toured a farmer's market in Minneapolis. It was as if he had drawn back the curtain so I could take a sneak peek at what mattered the most to him. On the latest trip, he'd planned a nature hike.

It was unseasonably hot for a September afternoon. "I want to show you where I used to take the kids when they were little." His eyes danced. "Since you shared one of your favorite places, I wanted to take you to one of mine."

Just then, the phone buzzed over the car speaker. "I got to take this. Would that be okay?" Cesar answered, using the speakers' connection, to confirm his company's furniture upgrades. There was no friendly banter with the female caller. An odd thought occurred to me—something that'd never crossed my mind before. *They've been sleeping together. No... this is clearly business.*

Cesar hung up. "Sorry about that. My company just got a generous donation, and it's my job to coordinate it." He paused a second. "She's someone I used to date, but that's over; she knows it," he said as though he had read my thoughts.

I relaxed.

"We're here!" Cesar said eagerly. He reached for my hand and headed down a worn path. I trotted to keep up with his long legs, smiling at his boyish exuberance.

The park was massive. Multiple trailheads, marked in an array of different colors, led off in various directions. He pointed out a few landmarks and told stories like when he'd taken his son for a ride on the children's carousel. "Isn't this great?" he asked.

A tall brown marker with a yellow arrow that read *You Are Here* stood at an intersection.

"We want to go this way." Cesar pointed up a hill. An older couple strolled ahead; we slowed behind them. The trail meandered around a few rises and then dropped towards a boardwalk that spanned the basin of a gigantic waterfall. The narrow, graying walkway ended just short of the roaring water. A row of families and couples waited to take a turn to see it up close.

I inhaled.

"Isn't this incredible?" Cesar said. We took a spot at the end of the line, he tightly gripping my hand. "I used to love to come here with my kids."

I bent close to hear him. "Yeah, it's really lovely."

While we waited, mist-like raindrops dampened my hair, and hundreds of tiny rainbows hung above us as though suspended on threads. Colorful blankets filled with families picnicking dotted a meadow behind us. Adults sat beside opened coolers and distributed paper plates and red plastic cups while their children played tag.

Finally, it was our turn. The wooden deck rocked with our steps' cadence as we neared the waterfall's edge. The roar became deafening. The water's spray kissed my upturned face. Cesar watched anxiously, clutching my hand.

"Let's take a photo here," he yelled before snapping several. Later, when I looked through the images, the untamed power of the waterfall seemed to capture the nature of our relationship—wild, exhilarating, and beautiful. Being in love looked good on me.

That evening we dressed up for dinner and headed for a nearby restaurant, a local spot that featured late-night salsa dancing. Though not good at sports, I was willing to try anything for Cesar. Since meeting him, my world had brightened, and colors appeared deeper.

As the hour grew late, the spacious dining room filled with couples. Soon the place was packed, and there were sounds of the band warming up.

"Let's get a spot," Cesar said. He weaved among the crowd to find a small space.

"Okay, watch my feet." He stepped forward and then back in a syncopated rhythm. He took my hands. "Okay, now you try."

I floundered.

"Like this. Step forward with your left foot, then back on your right" He slowed the footwork. "1-2, pause, 3-4, pause. Okay, your turn."

I matched his movements.

"That's right! You got it!" He waved his hands in excitement. I smiled, suddenly bashful, and glanced about to see if anyone had noticed. All around us, couples twirled in a complicated version of the same dance. The room moved like a swirling pattern in a child's kaleidoscope.

Our eyes met, and my cheeks burned. I looked away but wondered what he thought. Blushing, I peered up. He looked pleased, maybe even proud. I beamed and, for a moment, became the most beautiful woman in the room. Out on the dance floor with Cesar, I'd discovered happiness.

Until then, I'd never understood what people meant when they spoke of joy. My parents had discouraged giddiness. "Take it outside," they'd say whenever my sisters and I got too loud. Happy children were noisy.

The oldest of three girls, I grew up on a family farm. My dad would mutter something about his bad luck at having daughters. I knew he was talking about me—about all of us girls. When it came to chores, a female frame couldn't be pushed as hard as a male's. I was determined to prove him wrong. Every night I worked for hours without complaining, toting steel pails half-full of milk, waiting for him to recognize that I'd been misjudged.

Shortly before Dad died, he would weep. "I wasn't a good father to you girls. You deserved better," he'd say. I would wait to hear more.

For an apology for those earlier words. He would shake his head and wipe away the tears without saying more.

I had learned how to work but not how to play.

Life with Brad had been good but not joyful. Happiness was considered brash. I'd visited him at college shortly after we had started dating. Late one night, drunk on love, I danced a little jig in front of him. This show of joy was something new—a bold move.

"Stop it," he snapped, swinging his head to see who might have seen me make a spectacle of myself.

Crestfallen, I did as he'd asked, vowing to myself not to make a fool of myself like that again. Happiness took chances and was willing to cause a scene—all the things Brad had found scary.

The next day, Cesar dropped me off at the airport with a lingering kiss. I wanted to cling like a drowning person losing a grip on the last piece of driftwood.

Since meeting Cesar, life had separated into two realities: our visits and everything in between. Most days, I spent writing, having lunch with a friend, and watching nighttime television. Time ran together in a monotonous blur—each day a repeat of the last. I survived the boredom of the in-between by living on Cesar's texts. As the next visit drew near, I'd awaken; my body and senses would grow keen with anticipation.

"Gorgeous," Cesar texted after our last trip. "I may be gone for a few days. Off-line. My mom has been invited to a family wedding. Since her knee surgery, she hasn't been well. I'll probably have to go. I just wanted you to know, in case you don't hear from me."

My heart sank. "Thanks. What are the dates again?"

"I'll be gone the end of September. I'll try to message when I can." He sent an emoji of throwing a kiss. "I love you!"

"I'll miss you." I added a heart emoji of my own.

The calendar counted down, and then the week arrived.

Just as he warned, I received a few brief texts that wished me a good morning or sweet dreams. I kept my phone nearby with the screen upward so as not to miss a chance to chat. Each day dragged, but I survived with a reminder that he'd be back.

As the weekend came to an end, he sent several photos taken at the wedding. In one, he was dressed in a tux and held a mixed drink as though giving a toast. His wide eyes were wild with a look I'd never seen before. I thanked him for the gift but wondered why there weren't any of his mother.

5

HOOKED

"Love is not blind. Love sees everything and says yes to it all."
—Scott Stabile

October 2016

EXHALING, I GLANCED at the blank phone screen. Long-distance dating was killing me. Despite our growing relationship, Cesar often ignored my open-ended questions about his day and kept his answers about work to a few words. We would video chat while he took a walk or ate dinner and sometimes fit in a quick late-night call before bed.

At times he was hard to reach; the weekends and holidays were the worst. I'd hear from him first thing in the morning and just before bed. Some messages sat unseen for hours before he'd send a blast of replies, only to disappear again.

One night I'd missed his text by a few minutes. Panicked, I fumbled to respond. "So good to hear from you! How are you?" I watched the screen. The seconds turned into minutes. Mustering a bit of courage, I wrote, "Each day, I hope to connect only to discover you aren't reachable. Do you have any suggestions?"

"My love, I'm already in bed. It crushed me to read your words."

Crushed? I paused to consider what to say next. "I'm trying to figure out how to grow a relationship long distance."

"I don't know what else to do but try to be supportive while we're apart."

"I want to hear more about your life. To talk to you about mine."

"Please, I want to help, but you need to do your part," he messaged.

I blinked... *do my part? What's he talking about?* My hand hovered above the screen. Instead of writing a rebuttal, I turned off the phone.

Already in bed, I stared up at the darkened ceiling while my stomach churned. How do I tell Cesar we needed to do a better job staying in touch if this was to work? Our connection seemed tenuous and the contact infrequent. Cesar disliked anything that reeked of confrontation. After dismissing several angles, with a big sigh, I rolled over to sleep.

Finally, our next visit drew near. This time it was his turn to see me. He texted a few hours before his scheduled flight that there had been an accident at the job site and, as an acting manager, he had to stay.

My stomach plummeted. A nine-hour drive each way was too far to come for a single night. In my best fake voice, I said, "Maybe it's best we reschedule."

"Gorgeous, Gorgeous, I'm still coming! I wouldn't miss it," he said. "I'll make the drive, okay?"

"Really?"

"Really." He laughed.

I huffed with relief. "Oh, okay..." A warmth, like honey, spread over me.

His voice lifted as though smiling. "And, Gorgeous? Thanks for being understanding. It means a lot."

"Work is work. I get it."

Now, Cesar would arrive in a few hours. I stared out the window. The last rays of the setting sun lit the trees ablaze in the fall colors of vibrant reds and soft yellows of fall.

I glanced at my phone and willed it to ding.

The heating system kicked on; it sounded loud in the empty house. Devon, my middle son, had left to visit a friend. Cesar had requested we not meet each other's families until we were engaged or married. I agreed, though the rule seemed silly.

A few weeks earlier, Cesar and I had spent the weekend at a quaint little hotel watching movies, eating pizza, and hanging out. In between making love, we dozed in bed and chatted.

I woke in the early hours. Cesar was still asleep; his breaths came out in puffs, and his face had lost its manly lines in the pre-dawn light.

His dark eyelashes fluttered open, and a slight curve turned the corners of his lips. "Good morning," he whispered.

"Morning."

His gaze was tender. "I've never felt this way before. Not with anyone," he said softly. "Not even in the seventeen years I was married."

"Me neither." My chest swelled with all the things I'd longed to find—of being chosen, delighted in, and desired. I blinked away tears.

We had moved into each others' arms when he suddenly fell to the floor, his body coiled into a ball. His skin was clammy and slick with sweat, and he rocked back and forth.

I wrapped my arms and legs around his torso. "It's okay, you're safe," I murmured.

His breathing quieted, and skin warmed. Finally, he rose on shaky legs to climb back into bed. I pulled up the comforter and cuddled with our heads touching.

With his eyes still closed, he said softly, "I'm okay now."

"What happened?"

"I thought you were going to kick me." His voice trembled.

I pulled back. "What? Why would I do that?"

"Because of the way I was touching you." His caresses had been intimate but not inappropriate.

"Did someone do that to you?" I asked, my voice sharp.

He averted his eyes and nodded.

"I would never do that!" I clutched him to my chest. "I love you, Cesar," and added to myself, *And I won't let anything bad ever happen.*

"Love you more." His eyes flickered shut with drowsiness.

"No, I love you more," I breathed out.

At the end of that trip, I steeled myself for an abrupt goodbye, but Cesar pulled into the short-term garage.

"Aren't you going to let me off in front?"

"No, I'm going in with you," his voice resolute.

"Oh, you don't have to do that."

"I know, but I want to."

Cesar clenched my hand on the short walk as though I might slip away. I got in the security line and turned to wave but faltered. He stood rooted to the floor as though cemented. I glanced back one more time before the line disappeared behind a large column. Cesar stood, unmoved, with his head in his hands and shoulders heaving up and down. At the sight of my wave, he swiped away tears and gave a tiny wave back.

I'd scoffed at the idea of soulmates as hogwash, but Cesar had made me a believer. He was the first person I thought of when I woke and the last person on my mind before falling asleep. He'd become the very air that I breathed. My love for Brad had been built out of deep loyalty, but this—this was something altogether different.

Figuring Cesar was about four hours away, I checked my phone again. "Gorgeous, I'm nearing Chicago. I'll see you soon!" he'd texted.

Reading this, I vacillated between terror and giddiness like the sudden drops on a rollercoaster. During the break-neck ride, I'd vow I'd never do it again only to get back in line. This trip would be Cesar's first visit to my house. I'd wanted to give him a glimpse of my life, but I also had to tell him something. Something upsetting.

Since meeting Cesar, I'd begun to have doubts. At first, the worries were small nothings, but as my feelings grew, so did my concerns. The strange infrequency of his texts, his reluctance to introduce me to his friends and family, and the secrecy around some of his personal details were concerning.

When I asked how many sex partners he'd had, he replied, "How many times have I been married?"

"Four."

"There's your answer."

Losing Brad has made me paranoid. I don't want to be hurt by love again, I told myself, but the nagging feeling wouldn't disappear. Shouldn't people in love be confident about their partners? Unable to bring up my concerns to Cesar, I contacted an investigator, a former federal intelligence officer who had turned private eye, and asked that he check into Cesar's past, particularly his relationships. Was he divorced, as he claimed?

For the next several days, I watched my email inbox. Then, the letter from the PI arrived. For a long second, I studied the subject line before opening it.

My heart raced as I scanned it over. The stock note included an eleven-page document as an attachment. *Shouldn't I talk to Cesar instead of reading this,* I asked myself. *No, no, this way is better. Safer.* At the top of the page was a list of thirteen previous addresses. Was that too many? When Brad and I first got married, we moved six times in seven years.

Next were a couple of bankruptcy judgments, and at the bottom were several drunk driving charges. Cesar had mentioned losing a job a few years back, but nothing about the DUI's. Shouldn't he have lost his driver's license too?

The PI wrote he believed Cesar lived alone, though he couldn't be sure if Cesar was divorced since it was difficult to obtain those records. Each ex-wife, however, lived at a separate address.

My childhood home had thrived on secrets. My grandmother never learned her son had molested me. Keeping the family peace mattered more than my safety. I vowed to do things differently.

A car pulled up outside; I rushed out. Pieces of cut grass from the dew-laden yard covered my feet. Cesar swung me in a circle before sitting me down with a sloppy kiss.

"Sorry I didn't text more. My phone's been acting up."

"Maybe I can help." He handed me the device; I tried to reboot it.

"No worries, Gorgeous. Let's not waste our time on this." I returned it along with a kiss.

Already late, we headed to bed. Cesar took his time to arouse me while whispering how much he loved me. Both of our climaxes were explosive, and we fell asleep in each other's arms, spent. I snuggled close to his sleeping body, struck by the rightness of having him in my home beside me.

The following day, I started breakfast while he finished dressing. As I gathered the ingredients for pancakes, I spied his phone charging on the countertop. With a few minutes to spare, I plugged the device into my laptop and forced it to reboot.

Cesar walked in. "What are you doing?"

"I fixed it! It works." I smiled proudly with the phone held out.

He stared at it, pulling his brows together. "How?"

"Oh, with some software. It was easy, only took a second or two."

"Did you have to do anything special?"

Unsure what he was asking, I replied, "I think it made a quick backup and then ran the program."

"Where's the backup?"

"I have no idea." I waved my hand dismissively. "Why? Is that a problem?"

"No, no... I'm just curious, in case I run into the same issue again." He stared hard.

In a too cheerful voice, I said, "Hey, breakfast is about ready. You hungry?"

Still frowning, Cesar sat at the kitchen table. I placed a plateful of pancakes and eggs in front of him, then glanced at the kitchen clock. The hour was late.

"Yum, something smells wonderful!" he said, his warm demeanor back.

"I learned it from my grandma. She used to serve pancakes piping hot and smothered in my dad's maple syrup." I untied my apron to join him.

Cesar bowed his head and said grace. The room went silent as we took our first bite.

"Delicious." He smiled sheepishly. "Normally, I'm not of fan of pancakes, but these are really good."

"What?" I said, astonished. "You tried these for me?"

His face flushed.

My heart sped up as I searched for the right words. "I have something to tell you. I hope you'll understand why I did it."

Cesar looked up, puzzled. "Oh?"

"I hope that if I were your daughter, you would applaud my actions." I watched him.

He sat up straighter; his body stiffened. "Okay...?"

In a rapid burst, I said, "I ran a background check on you." The words hung in the air.

"Okay...?" He spoke in a slow purr. Cautious. "So, what did you learn?"

His wariness reminded me of a tomcat circling an opponent.

"That you moved a lot. You live alone. And that you have a bankruptcy judgment against you and several charges of drunk driving."

"I only have one charge of drunk driving, and they put me on probation for that. Years ago, someone stole my ID and green card. I still have the police report as evidence. Those other charges aren't mine." Cesar's tone was curt. Then he paused. "Yes, I had a bankruptcy almost ten years ago. I lost my job and my savings. I think I told you about that." His stare was piercing as if to burn a hole through me. "What else?"

This had been a mistake.

"That's it. That's all it showed," I said. "Oh, and that you own property in Texas."

"No, I don't. That property must belong to the person impersonating me." Rage rolled off him.

"You understand why I did it, right? Please say you get it." I reached out to touch his arm; he jerked back.

"I wished you'd asked me first." His voice was firm.

The tattered pieces of my napkin filled my lap. "I do too. I have to be careful. You understand." Though the admission that I questioned his motives for this relationship remained unspoken, a knowing look passed between us. I scrambled to think of something to fix this. Tears welled up.

Cesar stiffly rose to loom over me; his napkin fell to the floor.

Suddenly I aged backward and was a young girl again. My head drooped, and the tears fell.

Cesar walked away. "C'mere." His voice, now soft, came from behind me.

I shuffled to join him on the couch.

He lifted my chin until our eyes met. "Listen, Gorgeous. I love you more than you know."

"I know." I lost myself in his eyes before burying my face in his chest. His sweet scent filled my nose; the tears fell faster.

He rocked me slowly back-and-forth until my sobs quieted and then pulled out a cloth handkerchief. "Here, let's dry your eyes." I met his gaze again—his face still stern. "Next time, talk to me if you have concerns, okay?"

I nodded yes.

Cesar pulled me across his full length. The shape of his masculine body pressed against mine. His hard kiss seemed to say "I forgive you." I continued to cry, this time out of gratitude. The tears mixed with our kiss, making it taste salty and sweet at the same time.

6

COMPROMISES

"I want to be in a relationship where you telling me you love me is just a ceremonious validation of what you already show me."
—Steve Maraboli, *Life, the Truth, and Being Free*

Late November–Mid-December 2016

I LOOKED AT the calendar. Four months. It had been four months since I first met Cesar, but it seemed like forever. I had found my other half.

Like a mind-reader, Cesar brought up marriage. "I love you, but I want to wait."

"What are you thinking?"

"Two years." He waited for a beat. "At least."

My eyes widened. "Really?"

"I've rushed things before and don't want to make that mistake again," he said.

"Don't you think it takes more than spending time to know if marriage is right," I said. "And there's nothing magical about waiting two years."

"True," Cesar said, frowning.

"Doesn't it bother you we're having sex?" I paused. "As a Christian, I mean." My neck burned.

Cesar blew out a long breath. "Listen, God understands we aren't perfect..." His voice trailed off. "Did you know I used to pastor a small Hispanic church?"

"Really?" I jerked up.

"Don't sound so surprised," he chuckled. "It was a small congregation." He seemed lost in thought. "God understands us better than we think... and forgives. But... I'll support whatever you decide about sex."

I considered him for a moment.

Sex had been the basis of my intimacy with Brad—the glue that held us together. It had rubbed off the rough edges of our marriage while adding vitality. To forgo sex was unthinkable, yet I was plagued with guilt. The simplest solution was to convince Cesar to legitimize our relationship.

"How about I come to stay between Thanksgiving and Christmas?" I asked him. "I'll find a nearby rental for a short stay. Say three weeks?"

"That's a great idea, Gorgeous!" Cesar said excitedly.

"We could get ready for the holidays together!" I imagined us shopping for gifts.

"Remember, Gorgeous, I don't celebrate Christmas."

"But maybe we could start a new tradition. Something of our own."

"Maybe..."

Two weeks before my arrival, Cesar called. "Gorgeous, I'm moving to Illinois! I got a new job."

I inwardly groaned when I heard the location. Rockford was a town in the middle of nowhere. "What about my rental reservation?"

"Can't you cancel it?" he asked.

"The policy was pretty strict."

"Just stay with me. The company is putting me up," he said. "That way, you don't have to spend more money."

"You sure?"

"You have to ask?" He laughed.

Late Thanksgiving weekend, I pulled into the extended-stay motel's parking lot on the outskirts of Rockford, tired from driving hours in the sleeting rain. I rolled my tense shoulders. The motel's plain brick exterior jutted up like a nondescript square box. There was a steady hum of traffic from the nearby highway.

Cesar walked towards me. "Let me show you the room first, and then I'll come back for your luggage. Sound okay?" he said.

I nodded wearily.

He swung the door open. "Here's your new home away from home!"

I stepped into a room that included a kitchenette. A full-size mattress on a wire bed frame sat in the center, across from a cheap dresser made of particleboard. A small TV sat perched on top. To one side was a one-burner stovetop and microwave, and opposite, an iron pipe jutted out from the cement wall, acting as a closet.

Cesar opened the top dresser drawer. "I've cleared a spot for you," then pointed over to where his work clothes hung, "and left space for your clothes there." He seemed unfazed by its seediness. "Let's get you registered, so you'll have an extra key."

At the entrance, an older woman sat behind a safety-glass window. She put down an oversized fast-food cup at the sight of us. Hot pink lipstick stained the end of the straw.

Cesar bent his head to speak through a small opening. "This is my girlfriend. She'll be staying with me for the next few weeks."

The woman smiled. "Nice to meet you, dear. Your name?"

I stepped closer. "Kerry, my name is Kerry."

"I'll need your ID, miss." She chewed a wad of bubblegum; it snapped with a loud pop.

Pink-cheeked, I pawed through my purse. Cesar looked on with a grin. My heart sank at the thought of playing house. *This is a bad idea.* With an awkward smile, I handed her my ID.

That night, as we cuddled close, I stared into the dark before rolling over. The bed complained.

The shrill sound of a phone alarm woke me. The room was still pitch black in the wee morning hours.

"Go back to sleep, Gorgeous. It's early." Cesar patted my thigh. "Time for me to go to work. Someone's got to earn money around here." He snickered and rose, rocking the bed's frame. Lights flicked on and off as he moved about. A few minutes later, he plopped back down on the corner, bouncing me, to pull on his trousers. My sisters used to do this to bait me. I refused to give them satisfaction by pretending to sleep. Brad would tiptoe through the bedroom so as not to wake me. Cesar pressed his warm lips against my face. "See you later."

When the door closed, I sat up. *That's it? No plans, no discussion? He didn't even tell me what time he'd be home.*

The sudden whirring of the heater's fan broke the silence. I got ready and considered what to do with the empty day. I busied myself watching TV and working on a craft project I'd brought from home.

For the next couple of days, Cesar left early to return after dark. Each night, he'd step through the door, his clothes covered in dust. He'd pull off his work boots and exhale. Fatigue had turned his skin gray and sunken his eyes. While we ate dinner, I'd ask a few questions about the new job. He kept his answers short. Once the meal was over, he'd do the dishes. "Gorgeous, I still have a lot of work," he'd warn. He would stay up late, returning phone calls and emails.

Mid-week, Cesar's phone rang. He sat up to answer, with a glance at the clock; it read two in the morning. "What?" His voice was raspy with sleep. "Say that again?" He snatched his clothes, still listening, then hung up. "Gorgeous, I gotta go. There's a fire at work. The Fire Department's been called." He bent to kiss me. "I don't know when I'll be back," and rushed out.

He came home several hours later, covered in soot and ash, and smelling of smoke. He collapsed, exhausted, to nap before heading back. For the rest of the week, the after-hour emergency calls continued. Cesar drove to the site to check for breakouts in the smoldering wreck. I accompanied him on a few of the midnight runs.

But things changed. Cesar would abruptly stop working, mention the hour, and turn off the lights. One time, he plunged the room into blackness while I fiddled on a project. Most nights, he was sound asleep by the time I slid next to him.

I tried to occupy myself with a book or TV while waiting for signs that he missed me. Loneliness fueled a growing need. *Wait until tomorrow. It'll be different,* I told myself. *We're sure to do something fun this weekend.*

Cesar entered the hotel room late Thursday evening. Despite looking fatigued, he smiled. "You'll never guess who called today."

I asked, "Who?"

"Remember I told you my son lives in Rochester?"

I nodded.

"I didn't get to see him over Thanksgiving. Well, he wants to see me this weekend!" Cesar said excitedly.

"Oh?"

"You don't mind, right? I'll leave early on Saturday and be back Sunday evening."

I stared, confused. "You're planning to leave early Saturday and come back late Sunday night?" My chest squeezed. "Our first opportunity to be together?"

"Yeah, that's okay, right?" His voice lowered to a growl. "No one's coming between me and my kid."

61

I went still. "No one is trying to get between you and your son. I'm only here for two weekends, and so far, we haven't seen much of each other."

Cesar stormed out of the room.

My mouth tasted sour as I fought back the tears. I could tough out the weekend alone, plead with him not to go, or leave for home. I shook my head. None of these options were good.

Cesar re-entered, wrapped in a towel with his wet hair slicked back. With a cold face, he pulled on a clean pair of jeans. I waffled with what to say.

We went to bed in a strained silence.

The next morning Cesar readied for work while I pretended to be asleep. He left without a kiss. I pulled the empty suitcases from under the bed, still unsure of my plans, and packed. Then, I stuffed them back out of sight. Leaving would most likely end the relationship. *Did I want that?* Until now, things had been sweet. *Is it fair to throw something away because of a few bad days?*

Cesar came home at lunchtime.

"Can we talk?" My words came out in a rush.

"Talk about what?" He stopped; his height soared.

"This weekend."

"What about it?" He curled his hands on his hips as though readying for a fight.

"This is one of my two weekends here, and we've had so little time together," I pleaded.

"You're saying, I'm not to see my son?" His voice rose again.

"Of course not, but isn't there another way?"

"Well, I'm not introducing you to him if that's what you're suggesting."

"Okay...?" I paused.

Cesar left again, but on his return, his mood had shifted. "I do have an idea." His voice softened as if he'd not only washed his hands but changed his perspective. "Would you consider waiting in a hotel while I visit my son? That way, we'll have the car ride and an evening together," he said.

"Okay..." I nodded, relieved.

"You would do that?"

"Yeah, that works." His willingness to find a compromise had helped to set things right.

Once on the road, I glanced over at him. He watched the highway, his face rigid. After discarding several opening lines as silliness, I read a book aloud to break the tension.

Cesar listened with a thoughtful look. "Thanks for being willing to do this, Gorgeous. I haven't said much about my son, but we haven't been close since the divorce. He turns down most of my invitations— that's why this matters so much." His voice became husky. "Your support means a lot."

And I thought of packed suitcases hidden beneath the bed and was grateful I'd said nothing.

"You hungry? I haven't had lunch. Mind if we stop at a cafe?" he asked.

"Sure, sounds good."

At a roadside diner, we chatted, laughing several times, our previous closeness back. Cesar dropped me off at the same motel where we'd stayed before.

"See, remember the fireplace?"

"Uh-huh..." I said, dreading his goodbye.

"Well, I'll see you later tonight."

The room grew cold in his absence. As the credits rolled on the first movie, I considered starting a second, but my ears rang. Hungry and needing to clear my head, I left in search of a restaurant.

The winter wind gusted pelts of snow. Shivering, I zipped the jacket's collar shut and barreled head-down towards a nearby strip mall. A bell jangled as I entered the small food joint. Everyone turned to stare.

Plastic-coated red and white checkered toppers covered square tables. A pale-yellow glow of fake candle votives flickered. The place was more of a dingy bar than a restaurant. *I can't eat here.* I ordered a hamburger to go. A few minutes later, the bartender handed me a bag of hot food.

I watched another movie. It had turned dark. Then I finished a third—still no Cesar. The hour grew late, and my phone sat quiet.

Near midnight, he returned and crawled into bed, fully clothed. After a night of tossing and turning, he awoke the next morning feverishly hot. "My son's not free to meet for our usual breakfast, so let's head home," he said in a gravelly voice. "We can grab something on the way."

This was the first I'd heard of these plans.

"You drive, okay?" He handed me the keys. "I'm not feeling so good." By the time we were on the highway, Cesar was snoring, fast asleep.

Alone with my thoughts during the long drive back, I pondered our relationship. The way Cesar handled this weekend was hurtful. Dismissive. Long-distance dating wasn't working. We needed something more normal.

If I was honest, I wasn't happy. The condo I'd moved to after Brad's death overlooked a large parking lot and lacked privacy. The nearby walking path ran alongside a noisy street. Every time I exercised, the sound of traffic drowned out my music. I needed a fresh start. Someplace no one knew me as part of "Brad and Kerry." The community that had nurtured my family wasn't equipped to support a grieving widow.

Cesar woke as I pulled off the interstate. The following day, he left early for work, his fever gone.

Bored, I again entertained going home but didn't want to have to explain why I'd come back early. Only a few cars littered the parking lot. The cold sunlight bounced off the roof of mine like an invitation. I looked up the directions to the nearest ice cream shop. The neon-orange awning made the place easy to spot. Brightly colored tables covered the shop's parlor like oversized lollipops. The room was empty except for a teenager cleaning melted ice cream off a table.

"Hello!" She glanced sideways at me.

"Hi! I thought I'd stop in for a treat," I said, hungry for conversation.

"Great! I'll be with you in a sec." She threw the sponge into a small bucket filled with sudsy water and wiped her wet hands on the short apron. From behind a long bin filled with ice cream, she asked, "Care for a sample?"

"You live in Rockford long?"

"All my life!" She tossed her head; her ponytail bobbed.

"What's it like? I'm from out of state."

"Oh, I love it here. Everyone is nice. Not kinda nice, but really nice." She chuckled as though she'd made a joke.

I sat in the corner and watched her work while I ate. The same friendliness she'd shown permeated the town, from the grocery store cashier to the gas station attendant and the laundromat's manager.

I'd considered moving after Brad had died. It had been his job to construct several of my hometown's public buildings. Once a source of pride, now they acted as a visual reminder that he was gone.

But move where? Was I to toss a coin on a large map of the United States? A stranger to most of the continental USA, this city was as good as any, with its sunny skies and unassuming attitude. I got the number of a realtor from a friend. Maybe Cesar and I could start over. Date like ordinary people. Without discussing it with him, I toured several new homes for sale.

Things remained tense between him and me. Each night he worked until late and ignored the few times I hinted about sex. The three-week experiment had backfired. Instead of convincing him to marry me, I was no longer sure if I wanted us to be a couple.

I called Devon. "I have a weird question. Would you be willing to move?" The phone went dead silent.

"Mom, I haven't said anything to you, but I'm really depressed. There are signs of Dad everywhere. I'm game." His sad voice sounded relieved.

"Really?... Well, let's plan to move right after the holidays."

He exhaled. "Great."

Devon had said what I'd been feeling.

On the last morning, I packed before the sun rose. Cesar watched and then walked me to the car. With a small smile, he said, "Drive carefully and let me know when you arrive home." His kiss was a soft peck that seemed to say so-long more than see-you-soon.

The sun came up as I headed home. It painted the horizon a mix of purples and rosy reds. My life was at a crossroads. In the stillness, I realized I didn't care which direction I headed as long as it was a new one.

7

RESTLESS

"What's past is prologue."
—William Shakespeare, *The Tempest*

January–February 2017

THE SECOND CHRISTMAS without Brad was finally over.

The previous year we escaped the holiday by spending it at an island resort. This year I put up a small tree and planned a Christmas meal. Despite our efforts at joviality, an odd exhaustion hung over the festivities. It affected everything, even the way we handled the gift exchange. Instead of sitting around the tree to watch one another open neatly wrapped presents, we handed each other items still in their shipping boxes.

Brad, though rarely mentioned, haunted us. His absence was impossible to ignore, like an empty chair at the dinner table. Hollow-eyed, we talked too loudly and laughed too long as though trying to reassure ourselves that we were okay.

Losing Brad made no sense. Until his death, I'd believed everything perfectly fit together like puzzle pieces; now, I wasn't so sure. Grief had thrown me into a spiritual crisis. Barely able to cope with my pain, I was enraged that I couldn't fix my sons'.

Cesar and I texted little. Was there even an *us*? I took a rest from fretting about the relationship and focused on enjoying my sons as we adjusted to the new unwanted family constellation—one missing Brad.

Near the end of the stay with Cesar, I'd found a new home in Rockford. It was a split-level house with a small backyard thirty minutes outside of town. Its high-cathedral ceilings, dark faux-wood flooring, and pale light blue and gray colors created a cozy atmosphere. It had two floors, giving Devon and me plenty of space. All that remained was deciding what to do with where I currently lived. Not ready to sell, I jumped at the chance to rent it to a friend of a friend who needed a place to stay.

Cesar was aware that I'd moved but said little. I was surprised when he texted he'd like to take Devon and me to dinner, breaching his rule.

That evening broke the tension. Soon after, we returned to messaging. At least once a week, he'd invite me to lunch for a quick sandwich and even asked me to accompany him on a few work trips. After each shift, he'd stop by for a quick bite and would chat while he ate. On weekends he hung out to watch sports or help with a project. It was as though he'd thrown an internal switch. I liked the change but was wary.

One evening, after dinner, he waved me over. I leaned against his chest. "Things have been different since I moved," I said. "Not like when I stayed with you."

A thoughtful smile turned Cesar's lips upward. "After you left, I realized how much I missed you. I knew then I didn't want to lose you." He met my gaze. "I love you more than you know."

"I love you too, but those three weeks were crappy," I forced myself to say.

"I'd never had someone stay with me before." He stared off. "Then, with the new job and the fire, it was all too much. I wasn't ready." He met my eyes. "But I am now."

"Don't shut me out like that. Next time talk to me, okay?" I choked up.

"Okay, okay, I hear you." With a chuckle, he drew near to kiss me.

Meanwhile, Devon got a job, and day-to-day life fell into a predictable pattern. I found a local cafe for breakfast, a massage therapist, and a nail salon for a special treat of a mani and pedi. The realtor who'd sold me the house occasionally asked me to lunch. The adjustment to the new community was slow. Not a stranger to making big moves, I expected it would take some time.

A nearby church advertised a startup of a women's small group. I joined, hoping to make a friend or two. I arrived at the first meeting a few minutes early and sat down in an empty seat at a table of six. After a brief introduction, the other women's eyes looked in my direction. They gave a polite nod before resuming their previous conversation. *Once the meeting begins, it'll get better,* I told myself. The leader introduced a short series on Christian living. I listened until a leader asked me, "What do you think?" The other women looked away with disinterest. They stood as the meeting wrapped up and confirmed plans for lunch. No one extended an invitation to me. They walked out together, with me following a few steps behind.

Their closeness emphasized I was an outsider in a new town. This place was supposed to be different. I drove home, dry-eyed, but never returned. Moving hadn't fixed the isolation I'd felt since Brad's death. I wanted my previous life back. Since Cesar and I had agreed to no overnight stays until marriage, I went from waiting for his next text to waiting for his next visit.

As the calendar inched towards February, I suggested a getaway. "Let's take a trip! I want to show you Napa Valley."

"Great! How about we go over Valentine's Day?" Cesar winked. "Are you okay with doing some research?"

"Sure!" I grabbed the laptop.

He clicked on a link and let out a slow exhale. "Whoa! Did you know my favorite director estate has a winery?"

"No. It does?"

"Yeah! And there's a museum showcasing his movies." He rubbed his hands together. "Oh, we gotta go. Let's make it a special occasion! Would that be okay?" He scrolled through the online images. "Look!"

The restaurant's outdoor patio overlooked a hillside vineyard. String lighting created a romantic ambiance. The wait staff, dressed in black attire with white aprons, served gourmet food.

"Oh, that looks great," I said.

"How about I take care of making dinner reservations?" He grinned as though planning something special.

I smiled. *Might he ask me to marry him?* Before Christmas, the answer would have been no, but things had improved. I chalked up the disastrous three weeks we'd spent together as a bad patch of unfortunate circumstances.

Brad's proposal had been a spur-of-a-moment decision. We were inseparable during our college's last summer break until he returned to finish his final year of school. I started a new job an hour and a half away. During his first free weekend, he came for a visit.

"I miss you." He had stretched out on the bargain couch I'd found, lying on his back. "It's hard being apart." He scrunched his eyes close;

tears leaked from the corners. With them still shut, he asked, "Will you marry me?"

I stared, incredulous. This is it? No speech? No ring? Fighting the urge to cry, I said softly, "Yes." For the longest time, other people's romantic engagement stories made me ache with jealousy.

Cesar's eagerness filled me with a strange lightness. Like a balloon filled with helium, my feet barely touched the floor.

We landed at San Francisco's airport mid-afternoon the second week of February. The setting sun lit the Bay Area hills. Cesar gawked as we drove over the Golden Gate Bridge and wound around the hairpin curves. It had recently rained, filling the low areas with water. Everything was a bright green instead of the usual shades of brown.

Soon, we pulled into a small motel. Large flower gardens offset the place's retro fifties look. After checking in, Cesar suggested we go for a swim. Another couple was in the hot tub, sipping wine. We sat down nearby. After listening to their conversation, I asked their advice on the best places to eat. Cesar chimed in and, within minutes, had them laughing. His charm made me swell with pride.

That weekend we toured the area, ate out, visited wineries, and enjoyed a local tradition of a mud bath. On the last night of the trip, Cesar dressed in black dress pants and a white shirt, matching my dress and pearl earrings. He squeezed my hand as we headed to the winery; his clammy palms matched my own.

My first view of the place looked like an oil painting—dark terracotta brick buildings sprawled along the base of a rolling hill, framed by acres of vineyards. We drove through an enormous wrought-iron gate with the family's name welded at the top and crawled down a limestone gravel driveway lined with shade trees.

In the evening sun, the place looked magical. Fruit trees ladened with last season's red berries were adorned with twinkling lights. Walkways curved around patches of colored gardens with flowers covered in hoarfrost. The interior was just as impressive, with two floors of movie memorabilia from the director's various films. Mannequins dressed in costumes and movie posters lined the corridors.

Cesar spied several golden awards. "Look!" A grin stretched his face wide. "You gotta take my photo!" He looked at his watch. "It's getting late. Let's head back toward the restaurant." He pointed to an exterior side door as we neared the dining area. "I think it's a full moon tonight. Let's step outside to see."

I wobbled in the darkness. Cesar guided me to the guardrail. "See? The moon." I shivered; he drew me close. The moon's cool light washed over us.

"Isn't it lovely?" he said.

All I could do was nod when I noticed he'd knelt. In his outstretched hand, he held a small black box, opened to reveal a ring. The diamonds sparkled in the moonlight.

"Will you marry me?" he asked.

Time stood still.

"Oh, yes! Yes, I will!"

He pulled me into an embrace, laughing. His eyes twinkled. "I knew you were the one after you drove away in December. I was lonely. I found I missed you more than I expected."

For a second, the explanation sounded like Brad's. My smile wavered.

"Photos. We need to take some pictures," he said. We posed with my hand outstretched to showcase the engagement ring.

Cesar glanced at his watch again. "Oh, it's time for dinner!"

Suddenly, all of this was too much. "Hey, I'll join you in a moment." Once alone in the bathroom stall, I took a deep breath, and in the dim lighting, looked closer at my new ring. The tiny band of galvanized silver was topped with a few diamond chips arranged in a square. Its cheapness was surprising in light of Cesar's efforts. A few tears escaped. Had my expectations been unreasonable? Maybe I was being vain.

Cesar stood outside, waiting. "You okay?"

"Yeah, I'm great." I gave a weak smile.

He leaned to whisper, "I know the ring's not much. I had little to spend, but I plan to replace it in five years with a much nicer one."

I swallowed hard. "Oh, it's perfect."

We made our way to the dining room to be seated at a small booth close to the other tables and lit by the cold-blue fluorescent lighting. The menu featured typical American fare. The din of conversations was loud. I pretended to have a good time but itched to leave.

Two hours later, Cesar followed me back inside the small motel room.

"I think I'll take a shower," I said.

"No worries. I'll watch some TV." He unbuttoned his shirt at the collar and stretched out on the bed.

Where I undressed, sounds of a news program floated from the other room. The tears didn't fall until warm water pelted my skin. *Maybe we're rushing things.* An urgency thrummed inside; it pushed me forward. "Keep going," it said. "Do this and then that, and soon all will be right once again."

Putting on my best smile, I rejoined him.

8

RUNNING

Unfortunately, loving someone doesn't obligate them to love you back."
—J. Matthew Nespoli

Early May 2017

MOVING TO ROCKFORD hadn't fixed the deep ache left from Brad's death. Despite living here for a few months, I'd set plans in motion to move again.

I must have appeared crazy, wishy-washy, or maybe impulsive to those around me. I was careening out of control. Who was I? A mother of grown sons who no longer needed my watchful eye, a soon-to-be-married widow—single yet not— and a retired psychologist trying her hand at writing. My unfinished manuscript lay untouched for months. I was all these, yet none of them.

Cesar's long work hours didn't help. He complained he was tired and looked haggard. Our sex life had fallen off. Something needed to change. Like a horse feeling the whip's sting, I was bolting again.

Shortly after our engagement, Cesar and I visited a few Mexican cities to scope out their potential for a vacation rental business. When I first suggested doing this, he reacted with shock. "You're joking, right?"

"No, I'm serious. I've run a rental business before. Would you be interested in moving back to Mexico?"

"Yeah, I've dreamed of living closer to family." He spoke slowly while scrutinizing my face, as though sizing up both me and the situation. "You're considering this?"

"If you'd be willing." I left out the part that it had been Brad's idea.

Brad suggested it during the trip to Jamaica to celebrate our thirty-first wedding anniversary. By then, we had known he was dying of cancer.

For most of the trip, he listened to other resort guests boast about their golf games while he rested on the beach.

"I need to do something. Not just lying around," Brad had said. He tightened his mouth into a straight line.

I glanced sideways at him. "Makes sense." Though it didn't—these days standing too long made Brad wheeze. Cancer didn't just kill someone; it stripped them bare of all the important things first, like stamina, strength, and independence. "Why don't you ask the resort staff for a few recommendations."

It was mid-afternoon when a local driver met us in front of the hotel. He drove us through a few neighborhoods while sharing the area's history. Then he turned onto a steep road that wound around the hillside. The engine revved as we climbed higher and higher. Once on top, he pulled onto a gravel apron overlooking the bay. "Hey, you two need to see this view. Take your time. I'll be right here."

Brad eased the door open. He wobbled before finding his feet and then tottered towards the cliff's edge. I held my breath to keep from calling out, "Not too close!"

We stood side by side and breathed deeply; a tropical breeze stirred the dirt around our feet. Out beyond, the ocean sparkled a sapphire blue. We'd spent a lifetime together—so long that our purposes and goals had intertwined into one. All of it was coming to an end, and this was a goodbye of sorts.

"I can see you living in a place like this," Brad said, breaking the spell. "You could do that, you know? Move to someplace exotic." His eyes held mine for a long second. Then he looked back at the ocean, his face sad.

Cesar and I needed something that was just ours. *Something we could build together.*

After an initial reluctance, Cesar agreed. We made a call to the Mexican Consulate and soon discovered obtaining a visa would be complicated. I ordered reams of notarized financial documents from banks and investment firms and requested certified and apostilled copies of my birth certificate. One final step remained: an interview with the Consulate. Once they approved my application, I had two months to enter the country and begin the next phase. But there was one problem: the timing of our marriage wouldn't work to satisfy their requirements.

"Let's get married twice. Once at the courthouse as soon as possible and then again with your family," Cesar said. "Doesn't that fix the problem?"

I mulled over the idea. "Yeah, it does," I said hesitantly. The July wedding date couldn't be moved. The family had already made hotel reservations and purchased flights. "Okay, let's do that." I smiled broadly.

"We're getting married, Gorgeous!" Cesar shook my arms excitedly.

Once I'd finalized the late May civil service's details, I flew back to Michigan to wrap up some last-minute business. On the return, I realized, with a start, that I'd be married in a few days. Though outdated, to me, the vows meant I'd be making a lifetime commitment to me. *Am I ready? What a silly question–of course.* Some days I skipped about the house at the thought of spending the rest of my life with Cesar. *How could I've gotten so lucky?* He was everything I'd been looking for and more.

Is Cesar? Lately, dark circles lined his eyes. Thinking the problem was worry, we took a pre-marital assessment. The test result confirmed that we were a good match, but it didn't alleviate his stress. Most nights he fell asleep while watching TV.

"Are you okay, Cesar?" I asked. "You don't need to visit every evening. Stay home and get some rest."

"No, no. I want to see you."

"Are you afraid of getting married again? You'd said you wanted to wait two years, and now it's happening in less than one."

"I'm just tired, Gorgeous. Once we get to Mexico, I'll be fine."

The plane taxied to a halt. I strode through the small airport terminal, lost in thought, and searched the faces of the milling crowd for Devon's. To my surprise, it was Cesar who stood off to one side. In his arms was a gigantic bouquet of red roses.

"What are you doing here?" The words evaporated when I took one look at his pale face. He rocked back and forth on the balls of his feet and gripped the flowers so tightly that his knuckles were bleached white.

"What's wrong?" I asked. Images of one of my kids dying flashed through my head.

"I have something to tell you. I'll understand if you decide we're over." He screwed his face tight as though preparing to take a blow. "With our wedding this week, I went looking for my divorce papers but couldn't find them!" He began to sob. "And then I realized why... I'm still married."

"What?" My knees buckled.

"I know, I know..." Tears streamed down his cheeks. "Today, I filed for a divorce, but it won't be final for another month." His eyes went big. "Are you going to leave me?" A frightened young boy appeared in the outline of his face.

As I hugged him, I heard myself say, "Of course not." My mind slowed as I struggled to understand what this meant: then, it hit me. I'd been consorting with a married man. I teetered, suddenly dizzy.

With a shuddering breath, Cesar wiped his face with a handkerchief.

"You ready?" He grabbed my hand and, with his head down, charged out of the airport.

The thought, *I've been sleeping with a married man,* played on an endless loop. We exited into the bright sunlight; I'd shriveled in its glare.

Cesar held my car door. Avoiding his eyes, I mumbled, "No more sex. I will not be the other woman." He gave no sign that he heard.

We drove several miles in dead silence.

"Yeah, maybe waiting on sex is a good idea. But the timing of the divorce is tricky. Let's pick up the finalized copies instead of having them mailed," he said. "Once they're ready, we can make a day of it."

I gave a sharp nod. Now, nothing could go wrong, or the move would be delayed, costing us more money.

"Listen, Gorgeous, I'm sorry," Cesar murmured.

"I know." I exhaled, suddenly tired. "I know you didn't mean for this to happen," but added to myself, *this sure makes a mess of things.*

He pulled into the garage. "Things were so bad between her and me that I think I just wanted it over." He stared straight ahead. "I think when I walked out, I put the whole incident out of my mind."

Celibacy frightened me. Though Brad and I shared similar hobbies and interests, it was sex that connected us. We'd never been ones for long talks; we related on a physical level. Sex had brought us affection, closeness, excitement, and intimacy. It had been the thread that stitched us together.

Since the move, sex with Cesar had lost its passion. I blamed his work hours, aging body, and the stress of arranging the move. My Christian morals had kept me from fully embracing the sexual side of our relationship. I had hoped getting married would give me the permission I needed to explore; now that would have to wait.

None of this made any sense. *How could Cesar forget he was married? It was a yearly tax question.* I said none of this, though. A girl raised in the 1960s-70s knew better than to fuss or complain; instead, I threw my pent-up frustrations into getting ready for the July wedding.

The month flew by.

"I'm taking two days off for our trip to Rochester, remember?" Cesar said. "The reservations have been taken care of!"

As I packed music speakers, candles, and a pretty dress for the weekend, I pictured us enjoying a romantic evening to celebrate.

We walked into Rochester's courthouse together and, a few minutes later, exited with two copies of his new divorce decree. Cesar held up the paperwork in a show of victory.

"This is it, Gorgeous! Now we can get married!" His grin stretched ear to ear. "Aren't you excited?" he asked. He spun me around before pulling me into a big bear hug. His enthusiastic happiness wrapped me in a rare feeling of being wanted.

"Very," I whispered, savoring its deliciousness.

I unlocked our suite door and whirled to embrace him but halted at the look on his face.

"Hey, guess what?" he said in a tight voice.

"What?" I stiffened.

"My son wants to see me tonight," he said. "He gets off from work at eleven."

I gaped. "What?"

"I mentioned I was with you, but he's not ready to meet yet," He shook his head. "I'm sorry, Gorgeous."

"You said we could meet once you and I were engaged." My mind reeled. *When did this phone call take place?*

"I'm not ready to force the issue. But I promise you; he won't be allowed to do this after we're married."

A fight would ruin this evening. "How long do you think you'll be out?"

"I won't rush a visit. I'm not having my son think I don't want to see him." His eyes went cold.

My dad used to use this signal. My parents didn't often fight since what my dad said went. But when they did, fear saturated the atmosphere like a poisonous gas. There was an unspoken worry that if things got too out of hand, it just might not end well. Cesar once boasted, rather than confessed, that as he walked out on one of his ex-wives she'd clung to his ankles, begging him not to go. I took it as a warning that he was capable of doing the same to me.

Only a few hours remained before Cesar would need to leave. Hurt, shock, and rage squeezed my throat, making it difficult to breathe.

"Hey, there's enough time to see a movie. We can grab a bite there," Cesar said.

I stood, mute. *We aren't even going out?* I slipped on my shoes and followed him to the car like an automaton.

As we drove to the cinema, Cesar joked, his good mood returned. Still frozen in shock, I nodded here and there. He purchased our tickets, found the seats in one of the corner theaters, ordered food, then reclined. With bright eyes, he quickly squeezed my hand. "Gorgeous, we're back at my favorite cinema!" he said, all happy-like.

I'd become a nobody, benched like a third-string player—the backup to the backup. Instead of watching the movie, I stewed, getting angrier by the second, until I fell asleep—a trick I'd learned as a young child.

Dissociating had come in handy when the rapes began. Only four years old, escaping my teenage uncle was impossible. Years of farming had honed his wiry body. I got away by disappearing in between the crack of consciousness.

The sun was setting when we left the cinema. I gave Cesar a wide berth on the walk across the nearly empty parking lot.

"Aren't you excited about tomorrow's motorized tour of Minneapolis?" he asked. His voice was high-pitched, like a parent trying to coax a reluctant child.

The tour had been his idea, not mine. "Oh," I said. "Yeah, sure." *But I really wanted a lovely evening with you.*

I let Cesar's chatter wash over me on the drive to the hotel. He touched up his hair and added another spray of cologne.

"Hey, I'm heading out. I want to be there in case my son gets off early." He grabbed his satchel to leave.

"I don't know if I'll be up when you get back," I tossed out, hoping the jab would hurt.

"That's probably for the best. So, I'll say good night now." He leaned close for a quick peck goodbye.

My eyes shot open. Then he strode out, letting the door shut behind him. In disbelief, I thought, *There's no way he'll be gone long. We have early morning plans. He'll be back in a couple of hours.*

I watched television for the first hour and then the second. The mindless programs droned on. Then the third hour passed.

Any second now. He'll be fumbling with the keys.

Then it was four hours—still no Cesar.

I kept one eye on the TV and another on the clock. Finally, I tossed the remote across the room. "Where is he?" I yelled.

At the five-hour mark, I looked up the phone numbers of the nearest police stations and hospitals. After years of being taught not to disrupt others, it hadn't occurred to me to call Cesar until now. "Everything okay?" I texted.

No response.

"You leaving soon?" I added. Silence again.

I called next; it went to voicemail. Thinking I might have misdialed, I tried again.

"Hello?" Cesar answered. His voice sounded odd.

"Everything all right?"

"Yeah, yeah, why wouldn't it be?"

"Because it's late. I've been worried."

"I'm wrapping it up and will be back in a few minutes," he said tersely.

Weird, I thought, but said, "Okay."

Cesar stormed into the hotel room a few minutes later. "You won't believe what happened. I had to wait until nearly one o'clock before my son joined me," he said. "You'd think he'd tell me that he had to close the restaurant!"

"Oh, that's too bad." I fiddled with the edge of the hotel's comforter. "So, what did you do for those three hours?" My voice whined.

"I ate something at the bar." Cesar readied for bed, collapsed beside me, and promptly fell asleep.

I stared in disbelief as hot tears streamed down my cheeks. *Why wasn't today special to him?* Enraged, I contemplated ways of getting even. To pain him the way he'd hurt me. I could push him onto the floor or punch him. Maybe slap him. Instead, I stewed until sleep finally claimed me.

9

MARRIED

"Have you ever been in love? Horrible isn't it? It makes you so vulnerable. It opens your chest and it opens up your heart and it means that someone can get inside you and mess you up."
—Neil Gaiman, *The Kindly Ones*

Late June–July 2017

CESAR AND I walked towards the courthouse, an enormous concrete building in the center of downtown. With a shaking hand, I grabbed his to find it slick with sweat. We were finally getting married.

At the top of the marble staircase was the clerk's office. Simply dressed, with her hair pulled into a tight bun, a woman checked our paperwork. "You can have a seat over there." She pointed to a table behind us. "The judge will be with you in a few minutes."

It was then that I'd noticed Devon had already arrived. He wore the same suit he'd bought for his dad's funeral.

"Hi, Mom." He shuffled towards me with his head hung low and crushed me to his chest, burying my nose in his familiar scent.

Grace, the other witness, hurried in, barefooted and carrying her high heels. Panting, she gasped, "So sorry that I'm late!"

"No worries, we're still waiting for the judge."

"That's a relief." Grace slipped on her shoes and leaned forward to give a one-armed squeeze. "So good to see you today!"

"Thanks for doing this."

"Of course!" She smiled.

A voice came from behind us. "Are you the party getting married?" A tall, gray-haired woman, dressed in a starched black robe, stood in the doorway, her back rigid. "I'm Judge O'Neil." She smiled with her whole face, and her appearance's cold formality disappeared.

"Yes, we are," I said.

"We'll hold the ceremony in here," she said. She opened the door to a small room. Several dusty tables and chairs sat jumbled in a pile. The walls were bare, and the carpet dingy. The place smelled musty from being closed up.

The judge looked around. "You men, do you mind pushing some of the furniture out of the way?"

Cesar and Devon went to work clearing a small space. Once finished, they rubbed their palms together as if cleaning dust off blackboard erasers and passed a handkerchief between them.

"Okay, we can begin." Judge O'Neil opened a small book to a spot marked with a slip of construction paper and then read. The edges of its dark leather cover were worn, and the corners of the pages smudged.

I strained to hear her over the roar in my ears. She said something about commitment. That love was staying true to one another. She turned to look pointedly at Grace and then at Devon. "Is there any reason these two shouldn't marry?" she asked both of them.

My cheeks burned at the thought of Cesar's recent divorce. No one spoke.

"I now pronounce you man and wife." Her voice boomed in the confined space. She bent close to whisper, "Now I get to do my favorite—to hug you two first."

I floated out of the building a few minutes later—freed from the immense heaviness of widowhood. The joy on Cesar's face matched my own.

Cesar surprised me with plans for a quick trip to Mexico. The itinerary he scheduled was grueling, with early morning flights in both directions. He insisted we needed to do something to mark the occasion even though we had reservations for a longer honeymoon in late August.

"Plus, we can celebrate your birthday at the same time," he'd replied.

Despite misgivings, I agreed.

We flew out the next morning and arrived at a small vacation rental that afternoon. After setting down our luggage in the middle of the unit's kitchen floor, Cesar checked his phone.

"You have internet?" he asked.

"No," I replied.

"Me neither."

Looking out the rental's window, I said, "It's starting to rain too."

For the next two days, nothing went as expected. I tossed and turned on the bed's firm mattress. Most of the time, we were housebound due to heavy rains. Tempers were worn thin. Neither of us made a move to have sex.

On our last night, we readied for dinner at an upscale restaurant. Cesar stepped outside to hire a taxi. "Gorgeous, it's stopped raining. Let's walk." As we strolled the few blocks, he swung our arms back and forth to the beat of silent music.

We were seated at a table that overlooked the ocean. With the sunset, the sky had turned a midnight black. The moon shone through the patchy clouds and cast a long ribbon of light across the water. During the meal, I kept stealing glances at Cesar while he chatted. The candlelight illuminated his face a rosy brown.

He wrapped his fingers around mine and looked into my eyes. "Mrs. Morales," he said. "That has a nice ring."

Blushing, I dropped my gaze. "I think so too," I smiled shyly. Though I was keeping my legal name, I'd planned to use his among friends. Just then, a few sprinkles wet my dress.

"Uh-oh, it's starting to rain again." Cesar rose to his feet. "Gorgeous, let's hurry. Maybe we can beat the worst of it." We pretended to race on the way back, laughing. The clouds opened to dump rain on us just as we reached the building where we were staying.

I dozed, exhausted, most of the flight home. To my surprise, Cesar woke early for work the following morning.

As he bent to kiss me, he whispered, "I have to travel over the holiday for another factory's deep cleaning."

I groaned. "Seriously, over Fourth of July weekend?" Dread bloomed in my gut.

"You know, in manufacturing, the production line never takes a break." He chuckled.

The rest of the week flew by. Cesar joked with Devon as they grilled burgers, and the three of us watched the fireworks from our back deck. I tried to join in their lighthearted banter, but the looming trip soured my mood.

The room was dark in the predawn hours as Cesar dressed to leave. "Gorgeous, I'll see you sometime Sunday afternoon."

I clutched his neck. "Please don't go," I sobbed, hiccupping.

"I know, I know..." he whispered. "It's my last trip. I promise." He gently pulled out of my arms. At the sound of the door closing softly, I buried my head into the pillow to cry harder—this time in shame.

Fussing was taboo in my childhood home. My sisters and I were expected to work hard without "bitchin' or complaining." After getting off the school bus, I trudged toward the house. Outback of the barn, the cows were lowing, hungry. It was time to start the second day's milking. We dressed in silence, dreading the hours of work ahead of us. After pulling on worn-out clothes from last year, I would head to the milk house.

Cows no longer scared me, even though they were taller and heavier. I once asked Dad how much.

"Oh, about fourteen hundred pounds, give or take," he said.

My eyes went big like saucers. "You mean over a thousand pounds?"

"Yep!" He smiled at the sight of my surprise.

Dad had shown me how to walk up beside a cow all-confident-like. Not straight from behind where she couldn't see me coming, but from the side. With a quiet word and pat to her flank, I'd attach the milker.

I'd learned earlier not to be silly in the barn—no yelling or goofing off. Dad had lost his front teeth trying to train a heifer to be milked.

"Do I need to get the paddle out?" Mom would ask if we started to do what she called "lollygagging" too much. That was her favorite way of saying we were playing instead of working. Each time my neighbor kid would get on the bus, I'd try not to stare at what used to be his arm. Dad had said the boy had lost it in a farming accident. It was hard to look away from the large metal hook that served as his hand. He'd see me watching and would open and close its claw with a silly grin.

"When I say 'Jump!' I expect you to jump!" Mom would say, "Don't ask why or you just might get hurt or killed." Thinking of that kid's claw was enough to convince me she told the truth. Hard work and strict obedience were rewarded with Dad regaling us with tales of the latest mishaps over a pancake breakfast but fussing led to overhearing Mom and Dad discussing our character flaws.

Cesar returned home, looking tired, late Sunday evening. I looked for his dirty clothes but saw none. *Maybe he'd thrown them out.* I reminded myself that he'd spent the weekend supervising a factory cleaning. We snuggled on the couch and watched some TV. I waited for him to hint he'd missed me as much as I had him, but he made no move for something more intimate.

It was lunchtime, midweek, when I stepped out of the laundry room and nearly bumped into him. "What are you doing home?" I said with a start.

"I've been laid off," he said.

"Laid off?" I asked. "You just worked over the holiday weekend."

Cesar paced with giant strides. "They said they no longer needed me."

"Don't need you?"

He stopped to stare. "I thought you'd be happy. You've been complaining about all the work there's to do." He frowned. "Just drop it, okay? You're making me feel bad."

I watched him storm out of the room. Now that we were married, I'd hoped he'd pay for a few of the household expenses until the move. I stood dumbfounded. An uncomfortable but familiar feeling of fear stirred in the pit of my stomach. This was something my father would do.

Dad liked to take chances. Before I was born, an old-fashioned hay-baler nearly took half of his calf muscle when he used his leg instead of a pole to clear the jammed hay. Like a high-wire trapeze artist doing stunts without a net, he would do daring things that just might cost him his life.

Once in a while, he put the family at risk. I knew better than to say something. With my heart in my mouth, I'd get sick with worry as I looked on, helpless to stop him.

I did say something when I was sixteen. The road had turned icy during the church service. The car fishtailed as we turned onto the highway for home. Dad hit the accelerator and raced back at a dangerously high speed. The wheels glided across the ice, unable to gain traction. I gripped the armrest in fear for my life. Once Dad parked in our driveway, I slammed the side door shut, screaming at the top of my voice, "Next time you want to try to kill yourself, make sure I'm not in the car with you."

Cesar and I threw ourselves into getting rid of things. He went through old boxes from his former apartment while I sorted furniture and belongings to donate, sell, and give away. I tried not to cry as strangers left with my violin, cherry-wood spinning wheel, and stereo sound system. Each time it hurt, I reminded myself Cesar and I were building a better future.

The month flew by.

Two days before our July wedding celebration, Cesar stepped out of the bathroom. "Hey, I want to surprise you with something special, but it's going to take some time to get ready."

"Oh?" I said.

"Isn't it traditional for the groom not to see the bride before the service?" He lifted an eyebrow. "So, I think I'll reserve a hotel for the weekend and go a day ahead." He winked.

"Really, that's not necessary." I scowled at the thought of all the last-minute errands.

"Oh, no, I'll need to do this to pull it off." He nodded to himself.

"That's sweet, but remember, my family will need to be chauffeured." My voice rose. I'd been excited about Cesar finally meeting my mom and sisters.

"That's what the kids are for." He strode out of the room.

I sighed. In addition to my family, there were the flowers, the decorations, and the cake waiting to be picked up.

Just like that, my father would say "Enough," and my parents' arguments were over. My mother, always the loser, would look out a nearby window as the tears dripped.

Wives were to submit, so the Bible said.

"Doesn't that make us second-class citizens?" I'd ask my women's small group leaders over the years.

"Who wouldn't want to submit to a man who treated her the way Christ has loved the church? Remember Jesus gave his life," my leaders would remind me.

Cesar met me at the airport to greet my sister, our first guest. As he walked the two of us to the car, he said he'd see me at dinner. Devon picked up the rest of the family before leaving for work.

Later that evening, I picked up my family and headed for the restaurant, arriving a few minutes late. Cesar was already seated at a large table with a few of my out-of-town guests. At the sight of us, he swaggered across the room.

"Gorgeous!" he bellowed and pulled me into a hug.

"This is my mom," I said.

"Now I see where Kerry gets her good looks," Cesar said to her.

She giggled, blushing.

During dinner, Cesar kept the table entertained with stories. I watched with pride. A friend pulled me aside as we prepared to leave.

"You got quite a catch there! The next time my husband and I are in Mexico, let's visit."

"Oh, we'd love that," I said.

Cesar escorted me to the car with his arm through mine. "Well, this is it, Gorgeous! Tomorrow we get married... again!" He laughed at his own joke.

"Yep!" I looked away, upset. *Can't he see all that's left undone? Why is he leaving all the last-minute errands to me?*

"So, I'll say good night, and I'll see you tomorrow."

"Please, Cesar, I don't believe the silly superstition," I said, trying to find an angle that would break through his resistance.

"It's better this way. Remember, I have a surprise to get ready."

Better for whom? I wondered. He waved from his car as I drove out.

The garage spot next to mine sat empty. Devon wasn't due home for a few more hours. My footsteps echoed through the empty house. The sound reminded me of the hollowness of Cesar's actions. He would do the sweetest things, like buying chocolate-dipped strawberries, only later to be callously neglectful.

In the dark bedroom, I ran my hand across his side of the sheets. Without his body heat, their silkiness was cold. My family had a legacy of men abandoning the care of the marriage's lifeblood to their wives—to me, my mother, her mother, and her mother's mother. Had Cesar joined their ranks? Why was enduring intimacy so hard to find?

The next morning, I rushed to pack an overnight bag, iron my wedding dress, and load the last of the supplies into the car. Cesar met me outside the venue's door.

"Gorgeous, this is it!" He clapped his hands.

"Yeah, I know." I smiled feebly as I grabbed the decorations from the car's trunk. A lock of hair fell into my eyes. With my arms piled high, I slipped on loose gravel.

Cesar rushed to take a few items off the stack. "Breathe, Gorgeous! It'll be all right." My friend Theresa met me on the other side and took a few more decorations from me.

"Hey, you!" she said. Though small, she enveloped me into a cocoon of her arms. Her smile crinkled the corners of her brown eyes.

"Cesar, you haven't met Theresa and Sam yet." I waved him forward.

"No," he said, brightening.

Theresa's husband, a quiet gentleman, shook Cesar's hand while his eyes swept over him with an appraising look.

Theresa extended hers. "I'm Theresa. Nice to meet you."

"Kerry has said so much about you." Cesar gave Theresa a warm smile.

Theresa had filled the shoes my mother couldn't. For months after Brad's death, she listened over coffee while I cried about the loss. Now she was here to bless us by officiating a second service.

Soon the room was set up. A slide show featuring the highlights of our relationship played in one corner. On the opposite side was a small table topped with an enormous bouquet of white hydrangeas and a chocolate wedding cake. Near the back wall was a long table covered in white linen—handwritten name cards set atop the white dinner plates—several vases of cascading hydrangeas decorated its length. An archway draped in gauze stood at the front of the room. More sprigs of white flowers hung off its metal frame.

Cesar put his arm around my shoulder. "It's beautiful, Gorgeous," he said. "You ready?"

I nodded. "You?"

He grinned a big yes back.

Seeing the hour, I rushed into the bathroom to change into my wedding gown. The sounds of people talking grew louder from the other room.

My friend Connie entered. "We're here!" she said. "Need some help?"

"I'm good." I stepped out of the stall and twirled. The wide poodle skirt of the fifties-style wedding dress flared to reveal the crinoline slip beneath.

I hugged her. "So glad you've come."

"Wouldn't miss it," she said. "I think we're ready for you."

"Just a sec." And I traced on some lipstick.

Under the trellis, Theresa offered a few words and then nodded in my direction. I started to read my wedding vows; the words blurred. After a few fumbles, I finished.

Cesar began to say his but stopped mid-way; his voice hitched with a sob. He cupped his head in his hands and wept. The room went still. Sam rushed forward to lay a hand on Cesar's shoulder; Cesar nodded thanks, and then he collected himself, wiping away the last of the tears with a handkerchief produced from his back pocket.

"I now pronounce you man and wife!" Theresa said.

Cesar swooped me backward with a big kiss. The room erupted in applause.

That afternoon we were served platefuls of roasted potatoes, grilled asparagus, and ribeye steaks. Its fat still sizzled along the meat's seared edges. The room buzzed with conversations. My mother said something that made Cesar chuckle. Someone would clink their forks against the side of wine glasses, the rest of the table would join in. Cesar put on a big show of giving me a peck, and the table exploded with laughter.

These had been the same people who had worried about me after Brad's death. Their relief that my life had been set right was palpable. With the cake served, it was time for goodbyes.

"C'mere and give me a big hug." My mother pressed me close until my nose was in her graying hair. Her dry, flowery scent made me long for days past. "I wished you lived nearby," she said. "I miss you." This marriage meant I was moving farther away.

"I love you, Mom. Thanks for coming." Tears welled up as I squeezed her hand.

"I wouldn't miss it." As she turned away, I glimpsed grief etched on her face.

My sons squirmed with embarrassment as I said goodbye. The large room that had been so full of life sat eerily empty. I looked up at Cesar. My mouth went dry.

"Ready for your surprise?" he asked.

I nodded eagerly. Tucked away in my luggage were two gifts of my own: a custom-made lace negligee and a masculine bracelet I had engraved with today's wedding date, along with the words "For Forever" in Spanish.

At the hotel entrance, Cesar produced a bandana. "Okay, no peeking!" he said as he guided me down the corridor. I giggled nervously.

Cesar pulled the bandana from my eyes. "Ta-da!" He waved his hands toward the room as though finishing a magic trick.

The sun spilling in through the windows blinded me. Suddenly dizzy, I steadied myself against the wall. Every surface of the room was covered in rose petals—the bed, the corner table, even the bathroom counter. Their tips were soft and fresh, with no sign of drying edges. Cesar's eyes twinkled.

I stared blankly. *This is the gift? It should have taken two hours, not two days, to prepare.* Fearing I'd appeared ungrateful, I blurted out, "I have something for you too."

"Oh?"

"Just a moment." I grabbed the boxes from the overnight bag and rushed to the bathroom. The soft lace of the negligee slipped over my bare skin. I paused in front of the full-length mirror. My freckles were barely visible through the garment's folds. My shoulders tapered, and my breasts were firm, but my waist was thick. I grimaced.

The TV turned on in the other room.

I walked out. "Okay!"

Cesar glanced sideways before turning back towards the screen.

I said a bit too loudly, "I have something special for you. Can we turn off the TV?"

"Sure."

Several rose petals squished beneath me as I scooted close to hand him a gift-wrapped box tied with a black bow.

He slowly opened the gift and turned the bracelet like a child unhappy with his Christmas present; it glistened in the sun.

"Thanks."

"See, I had it engraved." I pointed out the date inscribed.

"It's beautiful, Gorgeous." Cesar turned it around his wrist but said nothing more. I watched, unsure what to do next. He stood, unbuttoned his shirt, and fumbled to unbuckle his black leather belt. His pants fell to the ground.

"Me next." Cesar pulled the nightgown over my head, leaving me naked except for the thong. I stared at his bare chest.

He kissed me. Slow at first. His lips were soft. We walked like two people in a three-legged race over to the side of the bed. Beneath the sheet were rose petals. I bent to swipe them.

"No, no... I thought we'd leave them."

"Make love on top of them?"

"You don't mind, do you?" Cesar, already in bed, swung his arms out wide. He climbed on top of me with surprising quickness. I wrapped my legs around him the way he liked and waited for him to enter.

His soft cock curled against my crotch. I gave him an encouraging look to touch himself, but he rolled over to use his finger on me. This was supposed to be a shared moment, not mine alone. I hoped my arousal would stir him, but he looked away. My breathing became faster. I watched his face, wishing I could draw him into the moment. For us to move as one.

He appeared bored. I wrapped my arms around his neck and kissed him hard as the wave of pleasure crested.

"Good night, Gorgeous." Cesar kissed my forehead.

"Can I do something for you?" I asked with a smile.

"No, I'm good. It's been a long day." And without another word, he fell asleep.

With a bruised heart, I sat upright. *Did the ceremony take that much out of him?* I wondered. I grabbed the nightgown from the floor, hoping to hide within it. The sweet scent of decaying roses perfumed the air. A few of the red petals moved beneath me. I left them, no longer caring if they stained the gown. Tears began to fall. What was wrong? All the build-up about tonight being special, only to have it be this.

What if the problem is me? I let out a shaky breath. *Am I enough?*

Marriage was supposed to have fixed all this. To make me whole again. *It will; just wait and see*, I reminded myself. *Once the move is over, things will get better.*

10

ILLUSIONS

"There are two ways to be fooled. One is to believe what isn't true; the other is to refuse to believe what is true."
—Soren Kierkegaard

Late August 2017

"U H-HUH," I SAID, only half-listening to the hostess as she droned on about the resort's amenities while I checked out our first-floor suite. Its small patio faced the pool. A king-sized poster bed topped with a white goose-down duvet sat in the center of the room. The large bathroom featured a walk-in shower. Its golden tiles glistened under the recessed lighting. *Hmmm... this space might come in handy,* I thought to myself. Since early spring Cesar's sex drive had dwindled—*it's the stress,* I told myself. *Now we can spend the next ten days focusing on nothing but our relationship.*

A few hours earlier, we'd arrived to begin a much-anticipated extended honeymoon. It had only been a month since we celebrated our marriage with family and friends. In that time, we'd sold our house, booked our flights to Mexico, and gotten my international visa approved. Now we could concentrate on ourselves.

The sprawling Jamaican resort sat adjacent to a woodland park with the ocean on two sides. The lush greenery and long swaths of pink, yellow, and red flowers accented its Grecian-style white buildings. A row of restaurants, each featuring a different cuisine, created a quaint city block. At the compound's center was a gigantic infinity pool. Its blue waters seemed to stretch into the ocean's horizon.

The stark color of the beach's bone-white sand was blinding under the noonday sun. The only visual relief from its brightness was a smattering of thatched-roof *palapas* and canopied beach beds.

The hostess ended the tour at the suite. Once we'd stored our belongings, Cesar and I strolled over to a restaurant that served a buffet. Floor-to-ceiling ivory curtains that acted as the building's wall danced in the warm breeze. Neither of us said much while we ate. I stared at the rippling inky water only a few feet away and let my mind drift after a long day of traveling. The sun had set, and a soft buzz of nighttime insects filled the air.

Cesar linked his arm through mine on the walk back.

"Shall we check out tonight's entertainment?" he asked. "I think the musical medley starts in a few minutes."

"I thought we might create some entertainment of our own." I smiled flirtatiously.

"Oh," he said, sounding disappointed.

Back in the suite, I waited for Cesar to take me in his arms. Brad liked to nibble my neck while he undressed me. Saying nothing, Cesar slipped off his dress clothes and sprawled out on the bed.

I headed to the bathroom to dress into new lingerie that I'd bought specially. While I pulled on the short, white spaghetti-strapped gown made of see-through lace, I wondered about Cesar's plans. On our first weekend together, we danced while he sang into my ear. I checked my hair and make-up one more time when I heard the TV. I walked out with a deep breath and stood in front of its screen. In my best imitation of a pin-up girl, I posed with one hand on my hip and my other knee bent.

"What do you think?" I asked. Goosebumps rose in the room's chilly air.

"Lovely." Cesar cocked his head in one direction and then another, trying to look around me. "Do you mind if I finish this show?" My eyes flew to his face.

"No," I lied as I tugged at the hem, wishing it hid more.

"Come sit beside me." Cesar patted a spot on the bed.

I crawled across the bed's length to join him. The garment's fabric strained as though it might burst at the seams. *I'm such an idiot.* I considered changing but leaned my head against his chest.

With a start, I woke, unsure how long I'd slept. The room was strangely still. Cesar was staring at his phone. At first, there were flesh tones. The blobs resolved into body shapes, moving in rhythm.

He's watching people having sex! I froze.

Cesar zoomed in for a closer look, rewound the video a few seconds, and played it again. He moved with confidence as though well-practiced.

A notification alert appeared at the top of the screen. Cesar opened the message that featured a younger woman's thumbnail image and typed a quick response. Then, he switched to his photos and sent a recent one of himself. As if on cue, a picture of her returned.

I shook as though I'd been plunged into an ice bath. Fearing Cesar would notice, I breathed in slowly through my nose to calm my racing heart.

Cesar sent a few more texts before he resumed watching the video. Unable to stand seeing any more, I yawned loudly. The cell phone clicked off.

"Hey, Gorgeous, you fell asleep!" Cesar pressed a wet kiss to my forehead.

"I did?"

"Yeah, someone was tired, but looks pretty sexy!" He kissed my mouth.

"I'm awake now," I said softly, paralyzed by shock.

"I see!" He rose to his feet and began removing my thong.

Where are the words of love? The cuddling and touching? Sick to my stomach, I wondered, *Who will he be thinking about—one of the women or me?* Cesar moved his finger in a circular, in-and-out motion, tugging at the dry skin of my crotch.

Panicked, I reached for him. "Let me hold you." The fear of possibly humiliating him choked out my anger at being betrayed. A man made to feel ashamed was a dangerous one. He continued as though he hadn't heard me.

My crotch burned. I tried to crawl back to escape. The mattress's soft padding rolled beneath me, trapping me to the spot. I pawed for the blanket, but its edge slipped my finger just out of reach. *Fake an orgasm,* I told myself but feared I'd get it wrong. Tonight was supposed to be different. Special.

"That's okay," I said. "Please, hold me." Mimicking his earlier action, I patted the spot beside me. This time Cesar stopped. He snuggled close and, with a quick kiss to my forehead, fell asleep. My bottom throbbed in time to my heart's beat. *What was that?* Having no answers, I drifted to sleep, exhausted.

The next morning, Cesar watched me while we ate a light breakfast; his eyes lingered too long. I waited for the right opportunity to bring up what I'd seen last night. Several times, I started to say something, only to be interrupted. My gut warned caution.

In the late afternoon, we were back at the pool and sipping margaritas. Cesar sat on the pool's lip, dangling his feet in the water. He took a sip of his drink and smiled.

"I saw you watching porn last night. What's that about?" I said with a rare bluntness.

"Why didn't you say something?"

"I am saying something. I'm saying it now."

"No, why didn't you say something then?" He stared daggers at me.

"Because I was shocked."

"I'd prefer you to talk to me right away." He looked away to end the conversation.

I'm the bad guy? My rage flared. "There's something else," I said. "I'm not okay with you texting or exchanging photos with other women." I hadn't planned to say this part until provoked. Years of covering up other people's wrongdoings had taught me to protect their egos over my discomfort.

Cesar went still for a moment and then bolted for the beach. Once he returned, a tense hush fell over us. He played on his phone while I pretended not to care. As we dressed for dinner later that evening, the only sounds were the rustling and zipping of clothes. We chatted about nothing while we ate. The tension between us crackled like an overloaded electrical line. My shoulder stiffened against an unknown threat while I wished I could hide like I used to. Cesar linked his arm through mine on the stroll back to the room; his arm muscles were taut.

As I entered the room, Cesar said, "I'm going to go to the concert tonight. I know you aren't interested, so I'll be back later." With that, he turned to leave.

I stared blankly at the spot he had just vacated, smarting like I'd been struck across the knuckles with a sharp rap of the teacher's ruler. After surfing the TV channels, I dressed for bed and tried to read. At the sound of keys fumbling outside the door, I looked up, tense. Cesar headed for the bathroom to change.

"You interested in going to the pool?" he called out.

"Sure..." I said cautiously.

"It's a full moon tonight, and I thought it might be nice to see it together." The earlier coldness in his voice was gone.

"Yeah, sure!" I tugged on my wet bathing suit and followed him out. The earlier wariness had been replaced by awkwardness. I struggled to think of something to say. The warm night air was muggy; a light breeze lifted a few strands of my hair. The pool area was empty, except for a few overturned plastic glasses that had rolled beneath the lounge chairs. Its illuminated water shimmered in waves of pale blue.

I shivered, chilled, as I stepped in. The soft water glided over my skin, and I rose, weightless. I had only taken a few strokes when a loud splash sounded behind me. It was Cesar, swimming fast straight towards me. I kicked harder, but he was top of me within seconds.

"I got you!" He laughed.

"I almost beat you!" I wrapped my legs around his waist while he held me.

"But not quite!" His eyes held my gaze for a long second. "I hate it when we fight," he murmured.

I tucked my face into the crook of his neck. "Me too." He swayed us back and forth as if dancing. "I love you," I whispered.

"Love you more."

"No." I met his eyes intently. "I love you more."

"C'mere." He released his hold so that I could stand. "I want to show you something. Isn't it lovely?" He pointed at the full moon. "It reminds me of the night I asked you to be my wife. Do you remember?"

"Yes."

"There was a full moon that night too."

He draped his arm over my shoulders. For a long moment, we stood side by side in the silence, looking up at the sky together.

"You're right," he said, breaking the quiet. "We shouldn't have relationships with the opposite sex. I'm sorry about last night." Our eyes locked.

I buried my head into his shoulder again and burst into tears. *All new couples face misunderstandings in the beginning. It's a normal part of learning to live with each other,* I reminded myself. And once again, things were right between us.

11

SHATTERED

"The best way to find out if you can trust somebody is to trust them."
—Ernest Hemingway

Late August 2017

T HE TENDER MOMENT with Cesar out at the pool the previous night had broken the tension. We spent the next day lounging, teasing one another, and laughing. The relief was palpable. Our new marriage was back on firmer ground.

It was mid-afternoon when we stepped into the hotel room.

"I have a thought," Cesar said. "Would you be open to putting our phones away for the rest of the trip?"

I whirled in surprise. "That's a great idea!"

"Good." He opened the hotel's security box and waited.

I hesitated. There were several books I'd wanted to read. *No, this is better.* I squared my shoulders and placed the phone inside. Cesar did the same. He rolled the locked box's dial and then looked at me with a smile. *See, he's invested,* I thought.

Our phones stayed out of sight for the next few days. We pulled them out midweek to see if we'd missed any calls or texts, hovering close to the locked box.

"Look at this, Gorgeous." Cesar shared a joke someone had texted him. I giggled, touched by his show of trust. As my earlier concerns evaporated, our phones stayed out longer and longer.

The rest of the trip passed quickly. We took long walks along the beach, went sightseeing, and danced late into the night.

On our last night we returned to our favorite restaurant. It was dusk when the hostess led us to a small table lit by string lighting. The large, orange-colored moon hung low in the sky. Its soft light cast shimmering ripples on the calm ocean waters.

We said nothing for a long moment. My fingers ran over the tiger-eye necklace Cesar had bought me. The jagged-shaped beads turned. I looked up to admire his handsomeness. All week, I'd waited for Cesar to take me into his arms. As we relaxed, played, and lounged, sexual tension would grow only to evaporate once we'd entered the hotel suite. Tonight, he'd dressed in his black slacks. In a rare show of informality, he'd left the top button of his shirt undone. A few chest hairs curled out.

Our eyes met. "This has been a wonderful week, Gorgeous." He reached across the table to stroke my hand with his thumb.

I flushed. "Yeah, it has been."

"What would you like to order tonight?" a server asked, breaking the spell.

I looked away, embarrassed.

Cesar opened the menu. "I think I'll have two lobster dishes."

"Are you ordering for the two of you?" she asked.

"For myself," Cesar replied.

I snickered.

"What?" He stuck his lower lip. "The portions here are small!"

Still snorting, I nodded.

Reluctant for the evening to end, we ordered coffee and dessert. On the walk back to the room, Cesar linked our arms one more time. Fireflies danced about, and lapping waves could be heard above the din of the resort's entertainment. With rising desire, I met his warm gaze and wondered if we would make love tonight.

Once in the room, Cesar busied himself. With his back to me, he hung the last of his clothes. "Let's pack in the morning," he said, his earlier romantic tone gone.

I blew out a breath, frustrated. "Sure, fine," I muttered.

We snuggled close, facing one another. I waited, hoping he'd touch me. Instead, he stared hard. A haunted look crossed his face. I'd seen this expression before—each time, it frightened me. *What's wrong?* I'd ask. He'd only shake his head and tell me he was okay.

Tonight, he whispered, "I love you, Kerry." My eyes flew to his face at his use of my name.

"I love you too."

He slid his arm beneath my neck to cradle me. I kissed him and let go of the desire for more.

In the pitch-black room, I awoke, disoriented, and then spied the tall bedposts. I grabbed the phone from under the pillow; it read four o'clock. Among the junk emails that littered the home page was a notification of a message. Curious, I opened it to a blaze of blinding light. I squinted. Someone had sent a long note. The words ran together in the luminescence, making it difficult to read. I rubbed the sleep from my eyes.

It was from a woman. A stranger.

You're married to Cesar? Well, I guess the joke's not just on me but on you too. I've been dating him for the past three months...

W-w-what? This must have been intended for someone else. I checked the salutation; it was addressed to me. My heart galloped.

We met online. I got divorced a year and a half ago. Cesar swept me off my feet. He's been the first man I've trusted in a long time. The first man I've had sex with after my husband.

...had sex with Cesar? None of this made sense. I reviewed the past year we'd spent together—our weekend dates, the wedding, moving in together, and getting ready to relocate. *How is this possible?*

He took me to Minneapolis for a long weekend. I noticed there was a woman's sunglasses case in the car and asked him about it. He laughed it off and said his son's girlfriend must have left it. It's a bright pink and orange floral color.
On one of our overnighters, he wore a silver bracelet. He took it off and pointed to the engraving of "Para Siempre" and then told me that that meant "For Forever" in Spanish. He said that's how he felt about me and asked if I wanted to keep it. He said we had a forever kind of love.

I ran to the toilet and emptied my bowels with a sickening rush. My body rocked back and forth in a keening motion.

The cold drove me back to bed. Clinging to its edge, I pulled up the covers to quell the violent shaking. *She's confused and must be thinking of someone else*, yet she'd described our personal items accurately.

This summer, we met at a downtown hotel. He arrived late; we made love and then fell asleep. It was in the early morning hours, around 3 o'clock, when he got a call. The phone rang twice. He picked it up the second time. Was that you?

I'm sorry to break this news to you. I'm devastated too. You have my condolences.

I wish you the best. I truly do.

—Susan

The room spun like a top.

I live in Rockford and am moving to Mexico. I have three sons and am married to Cesar. He loves me.

Why would this woman lie? What did she have to gain?

I'm married to Cesar. He's a good man, I repeated.

Two planes of realities, like snow globes, collided. The first was everything I thought I knew up to this moment, and the second started when I read the letter. There was no agreement between what I believed to be true and what she'd described.

My world shattered.

In a brilliant flash, static, like an off-the-air TV channel, filled my mind. There was no time and no sense of orientation. I was nowhere and no one.

A strange sound awakened me. It was my teeth chattering. I glanced at the clock; an hour had passed.

"Cesar, Cesar, you need to wake up."

"What?" He rolled to face me.

"A woman wrote to me. She said she knows you."

His eyes went wide, showing the whites around the edges. "What?" He bolted upright. "What did you say?"

"I said a woman named Susan wrote me and says she knows you."

"Stop reading that letter!" he shouted.

"She knows you!"

He flew out of bed. "Stop!" he yelled.

I turned away, ill. *He knows her.* I could delete the note and pretend this had been a bad dream. My grandmother had erased the unpleasantries of her past by rewriting history. But it had cost her with years of loneliness and strained family relationships. Secrets often haunted their keeper like vengeful ghosts. How could I forget Cesar had had an affair?

I could threaten to kick him out but to confront him was risky. He had shown earlier this week that he was capable of ruthlessness.

The walls of the room started to close in on me. I slipped on my shoes and dashed to the beach. The sun had risen above the horizon, warming the cool air. I stopped to stare at the water. A franticness drove me to keep moving; I headed down the shoreline. Potholes left by yesterday's pedestrians covered the terrain. I tripped and hit the ground with a thud. Dammed-up tears broke free, and I sobbed.

Do I stay or go?

I dialed a close friend, a younger woman I met a few years back at a local children's 4-H club. Until recently, I trusted her wisdom but had forgotten in my panic that she believed Cesar to be an opportunist. I had no idea how she'd come to that conclusion since they'd never met.

She answered on the first ring.

"What do you think?" I asked.

"He's a con artist, Kerry. He's only in this relationship for the money." Her words cut razor sharp. "I'm sorry to be so blunt. This is probably the last thing you wanted to hear."

I grimaced. "Okay, well, please pray for me. I gotta go." And the line went dead. *Stupid, I should have known better,* I said under my breath.

I called my friend Theresa next.

"Go talk to him." She spoke in a low voice. "You are both in shock. I think you need to go back and find out what's going on," she said. "I suspect it's an addiction—a sexual addiction."

"Okay, okay." I hung up and shivered in the sun's heat. Like a surgeon's knife, Cesar's betrayal had split me open. Did I want to stay in this marriage? Where would I go now that the house in Rockford had been sold? My only home was in Mexico.

I headed down the empty beachfront and stumbled again. I rose to sit on the corner of a lounge chair. One wave after another surged in and raced up the shoreline. Their white-crested edges moved closer to my feet.

I had married a stranger.

Lost, I paced in circles and recited aloud a Bible verse—a passage I'd learned as a young child in my grandmother's Sunday School class. "The Lord is my shepherd. In him, I have everything I need." The loose sand churned; I floundered but caught myself. "In him, I have everything I need!" I said louder. An early morning jogger gave me an odd stare.

A new thought struck me. I was about to open a business in Mexico without the ability to read, write, or speak Spanish.

Flabbergasted, I dropped to the ground.

I no longer had a residence in the United States, and the airline tickets to Cancun had been purchased. If I walked away from this marriage, I would be back in the same spot I'd been in at Brad's death. *God, are you still with me?*

The first male I had truly trusted had been Brad. He'd restored my belief in the decency of men. I'd thought the same was true about Cesar.

"The Lord is my shepherd. In him, I have everything I need..." I whispered.

Brad had lost his life to cancer. *Is God good? Is my marriage to Cesar a scam?*

Cesar had told me shortly after we'd met that he used to masturbate on the job. Maybe Theresa was right. All of this was a cry for help.

I walked back to the hotel where Cesar waited and then paused. *What if this is just the beginning, and the worst is yet to come?*

12

FALSE REALITIES

"The truth does not change according to our ability to stomach it."
—Flannery O'Connor

Early September 2017

IT WAS SURPRISING to learn as a clinician how many clients had cheated or were cheated on—even more shocking was the number who stayed. Not Brad. He'd warned he would leave if I ever betrayed him like that. I thought I'd go, too, until it happened to me.

I returned to the hotel room to find Cesar bent over the luggage packing. He spun, wide-eyed. "Kerry, I shouldn't have said what I did. I don't know what came over me."

I stared hard.

His face crumbled. "Okay, yes... yes, I know her. Yes, I've been seeing her," he said. "But I swear I've never done anything like this before. I just wanted to see what having an affair was like." He moaned, "Stupid, I know," and buried his face in his hands.

Aghast, I took a step back. *You wanted to see what having an affair was like?* "I asked if you were scared about getting married; you told me you were fine!"

"You're right. I wasn't honest. I didn't know how to say that I was having a hard time." He slumped his shoulders.

"What else don't I know?" I tilted my head and glared.

"Are you going to leave me?" he whined.

With folded arms, I studied him. *Could I go alone to Mexico?* "I don't know what I'm going to do, Cesar." Exhaling, I ran my hands through my hair.

"I want us to work," he pleaded. "She's nothing to me. A mistake. I realized it right away but didn't know how to break it off."

I cocked an eyebrow at this. All week, he'd insisted we do things his way. He'd spent an entire afternoon and paid exorbitant taxi fees in search of his favorite popcorn, and he didn't know how to end an affair?

"Our shuttle is leaving soon. I have to pack." While I stuffed my clothes into suitcases, I mulled over Cesar's explanations. His excuses sounded more like lies than the truth. I rubbed my eyes.

On the flight home, I stared out of the passenger window while the woman's words replayed.

...he wore a silver bracelet... told me that meant "For Forever" in Spanish... said that's how he feels about me.

He'd used my wedding gift to ply for sex.

...we met at a hotel downtown... we made love, and then we fell asleep.

The month of abstinence I spent waiting for Cesar's divorce, he'd been fucking her. And the day we went to the courthouse for the decree, he'd been excited about their date, not spending an evening with me. I peeked at him. *Was there anything real about our relationship?* How long had he been on a dating site? How many other women had he slept with? How many times did he and Susan meet? *What else don't I know?*

Cesar's eyes were glued to the small TV display on the back of the seat in front of him. Sulkiness had replaced his earlier anxiousness; it warned there'd be a nasty argument if I pressed him too far.

It was late when we arrived home. A soft glow was visible in the direction of Devon's room. I considered talking to my son but knew it would destroy his fragile relationship with Cesar. I headed for the bedroom instead.

That night, Cesar wrapped me in his arms, gluing us together. I stiffened but lay still until I heard the sound of his snores. Could I trust Cesar? Was this relationship salvageable? I slipped out of his arms. *Play nice until you have a plan,* I told myself.

The realtor called the next day to let me know that the new owner wanted to take possession of the house and asked if we could move out. There were still several weeks left before our flight to Mexico. Devon was already relocating closer to his work. After searching online, I found a small one-bedroom apartment to stay in until we left the country.

With the last of our things loaded, I leaned through the opened car window. "Do you mind waiting? I'd like to walk through the house alone," I asked Cesar.

"Sure. Take your time."

At the back entrance sat the washer and dryer I'd bought. Lines on the carpet were the only reminders of my furniture. Now there were only bare rooms, bare walls, and bare windows. The place looked gutted. Empty. I had so many dreams for this home, this town, and my new marriage. It was supposed to be my second chance at a fairytale ending. But now, the house had been sold, and my marriage was in shambles. The couches, chairs, and area rugs I'd selected with care occupied someone else's abode. I twirled in the center of the last room. All I was letting go of spun around me in a dizzying circle. I slowed to a stop, dropped to my knees, and cried.

That afternoon we checked into the one-bedroom rental that would be our residence for the next few weeks. The high-quality website photos had hidden a shoddy interior. The bed's thin mattress flattened under two adult bodies. The couch's lack of padding made it uncomfortable to sit on for long stretches of time. *This is temporary,* I reminded myself.

I waited several more days for Cesar to say something about getting help before I brought the subject up. "Don't you think we should get some counseling?" I asked.

"That's up to you, Gorgeous. You're the expert," he said flatly.

But it's your problem, I thought. Since our return from the honeymoon, Cesar vacillated between an angry sullenness and being oddly agreeable. A sense of warning prickled that I better proceed cautiously. "Well, I don't know what's best, and whatever we do is likely to be expensive."

"What is it you want from me—with all this talk of money? I thought you wanted me to get better." With a roar, he leaped off the couch. "Fuck!" And he hurled his phone at the cement wall.

I jerked upright.

"See what you made me do?" He held the phone out; its glass screen was a web of cracks.

"What I made you do?" I said, surprised.

He charged at me, stopping inches from my face. "Don't you start. I will only take so much!" His face contorted with rage. With his bottom lip curled, he snarled, "You're lucky to be married to me now."

Quivering with fear, I averted my eyes.

He stormed out, slamming the front door.

I exhaled. For days, an uneasiness had been building. Cesar's initial remorse was over, and his patience with the situation was gone. He had made it clear there was a line I was not to cross. Cesar didn't have a problem with his anger; he had a problem with mine.

I could leave, I thought. *Tell everyone the marriage was a mistake.* Brad and I hadn't started on the right foot either. On our honeymoon, he had blown up over some small thing—I no longer remembered what—and punched me in the shoulder, leaving a bruise. After a year of intense marital counseling, he never hit me again. Couldn't things between Cesar and me be fixed like they'd been with Brad? *When is a relationship over?*

A nearby psychologist advertised a specialty in sexual addiction. I called for an appointment. As our first session neared, I oscillated between hopefulness and fear. What if I started to cry and couldn't stop? What if Cesar lost it again?

We took a seat on a couch in the basement hallway of a local church while we waited. Children's crayon-colored pictures of Jesus feeding the hungry loaves of bread covered the opposite cement walls. Tears burned the back of my eyes. I silently prayed, "I'm dying, God. Please save me too."

A petite woman with a pregnant belly waddled towards us. "I'm Dr. Sanders."

Once settled in her small office, she asked, "What brings you here?"

After glancing at me, Cesar spoke, "I cheated on my wife."

At those words, my head filled with a loud buzzing that drowned out the rest of what was said. I twisted a tissue in my lap while tears fell and waited for my turn.

"Cesar, I'd like you to complete an online assessment," the doctor said. "It'll give a better picture of your issues."

He nodded in agreement.

"Let's meet next week to review the results, and we'll make a plan." She leaned forward to clasp her hands. "I can't take you on as clients. There isn't the time with your upcoming move, but we'll figure out something, okay?" She stood, ending the meeting.

Wait, what about me! I mentally screamed as I followed her towards the main door.

As we drove back to the rental, Cesar asked, "What did you think?"

"I liked her," I said, unsure what he was asking.

"Yeah, me too."

My mind raced with confusion. Why had Cesar been the focus of the session? Wasn't our relationship the client? All the things I needed to say, all the pain at learning I'd been betrayed, and all the fears about what this meant for our future pressed against the walls of my chest. I feared the pain would tear me apart.

Over the weekend, we took a quick trip to visit Theresa and Sam. The last time we'd seen them was at our second wedding. Since the therapy appointment, Cesar's and my conversations were polite but stiff. For the first hour of the drive north neither of us spoke. I watched the scenery pass as the silence stretched. So many burning questions demanded answers. Several times I started to say something only to close my mouth. Good wives didn't corner their husbands.

"Cesar, right after we started dating, you went to a family wedding. Did you go with your mom, like you said?"

With his eyes trained on the road, he went still. The beating of my heart pounded in my ears while I waited. After a long pause, he said, "No, I met someone at a resort, and then she and I went on to the wedding." His voice was calm.

I swayed lightheaded. "What about all the company trips? Were those real, or were you meeting someone?"

"For one of the trips, I met up with the same woman I took to the wedding. Maria, her name is Maria. We've been seeing each other for a while," he said. "The other trip was with Susan, the woman who contacted you."

I stiffened in shock. *What? There have been other women?* Suddenly a new thought occurred. "What about the night before our wedding? You said you needed time to plan something special; what did you really do?" Coldness laced my voice.

"I slept with Susan." He said this as though placing an order with the butcher.

Struggling to absorb what he'd said, I stared blankly out the window as the blood drained from my face. Cesar had spent the evening with my family and kissed me goodnight before driving over to Susan's to have sex. The very next day, he made promises to love me. I panted as though out of air. All the oxygen seemed to have been sucked from the car.

Cesar glanced sideways. "Don't go asking questions if you aren't ready for the answers," he snarled.

I jerked, enraged. "I'm the asshole because you don't like my reaction? You're the one who did these things. Not me. You!" I growled, "How dare you!"

"Don't blame me if you can't stomach hearing the truth." He tightened his grip on the steering wheel; his knuckles whitened.

I sat beside him, devastated—ripped apart by what I'd heard. Sex wasn't something casual, like taking a piss; it was a sacred sharing of body and soul. Cesar's disloyalties had ruined its preciousness and broken my heart. Couldn't he see the travesty he'd made of our marriage? *Don't say any more, or it's going to get nasty.* But I needed to say more, or I'd become an unwilling participant in my own betrayal.

Theresa and Sam greeted us that afternoon with smiles and big hugs. Cesar's affairs were mentioned at the start but then left behind. We spent the weekend enjoying good food and watching sports. Though the weather had turned cold, we went for a swim in the community pool, splashing water at each other. The trip was a welcomed respite from our problems.

With a concerned look, Theresa hugged me goodbye. "Call me. Any time, okay?"

"Brother," Sam said to Cesar, "here's my business card. Let's keep in touch."

Cesar met Sam's eyes. "Thank you. I will." He flashed the two of them a smile.

A few days later, we waited in the basement hallway for our second therapy appointment. The same children's pictures covered the walls. I toyed with my purse strap in the heavy silence.

Dr. Sanders greeted us. "Good to see both of you." Her smile turned pensive once we arrived in her office. "Cesar, I've got your test results back. Are you comfortable reviewing the findings in front of Kerry?"

"Yeah, I'm okay with that," he muttered.

"You have a severe sexual addiction."

I sat upright. *Severe? How bad is severe?* I'd never heard of sex addiction until now. The United States medical community didn't recognize it as a mental health condition. Since Theresa had mentioned it that morning on the beach, I'd done some research. It wasn't a high sexual drive, as some people thought, but rather a way of using sex to cope. People with this type of addiction numbed emotional pain by pursuing riskier and riskier sexual behaviors. They jeopardized their jobs and marriages with excessive pornography, sexting, cheating, and other sexual activities.

"This level of severity warrants a two- to three-month stay at an inpatient or residential treatment program," the doctor continued.

I squeezed my eyes shut.

"There are several excellent US facilities, but unfortunately, they're not cheap." She paused. "I'll email you some information about each so you can see which fits your needs." She studied him for a second.

I struggled to keep up. *Several months of treatment?* I'd worked at two different psychiatric facilities. They provided round-the-clock care, daily therapy appointments, group counseling sessions, and doctor visits—all not covered by insurance. If Cesar went, he'd be the patient, not our marriage. And if we pursued this, I'd have to pay. Cesar had said little about his financial situation before our wedding; I'd learned since he was broke.

"Let me know if there is any other way I can help you two." She stood to say goodbye.

I blinked. *You'll help the two of us? Where are my tests? We haven't discussed what I need. No one has even asked how I'm doing.*

Cesar strode beside her as we walked out. "Thank you, doctor. We'll watch for your letter." I shuffled a few steps behind them and wondered if they would notice if I suddenly went missing.

On our drive home, Cesar's mood had lifted. "Well, that was interesting. Really helpful. What did you think, Gorgeous?"

Looking away, I replied flatly, "Yeah, sure. It was good."

That evening, Cesar settled down on the couch. Instead of joining him, I stood beside the bedroom window to watch the last of the autumn leaves fall. They weaved and twirled like fairies frolicking as they drifted down. The ones on the ground laid lifeless and soon would be swept up to be thrown away. That was me; I'd been forgotten. Discarded.

Like a life-sized paper doll, I walked and talked as though all was normal. Underneath this facade was a growing fragility, and it wouldn't take much to finish destroying me.

The room grew dark. Instead of turning on the light, I flopped onto the bed and typed into the phone's browser *intensive treatment programs for sex addiction*. A small list of options appeared; one was a highly rated three-day program. The words "couples" and "Christian" jumped out at me. After sending the program director a brief note for more information, I buried my face into a pillow and sobbed.

13

HELP

"The truth is rarely pure and never simple."
—Oscar Wilde, *The Importance of Being Earnest*

Early October 2017

MY HEART RACED as I stepped out of the car.
Cesar reached for my hand. "Ready?"

Without saying a word, I followed him across the gravel parking lot towards a squat one-story brick building where it sat tucked among a grove of trees. Ten days ago, I contacted this sexual addiction program. In less than a week, we were moving to Mexico.

The large lobby was carpeted in soft blues, with several sofas and armchairs scattered about the room. The clerk's window to the right was dark and empty. Against the far wall was a set of doors that most likely led to offices.

A tall, gray-haired gentleman intercepted us. "Cesar and Kerry?"

"Yes?" Cesar said.

"I'm a counselor here. Why don't you take a seat?" He waved towards the general area. "We'll get started in a few minutes." He disappeared behind one of the closed doors.

Other couples of all ages dotted the room. The hunched-over women wore a beaten-down expression accompanied by blank-faced men who resembled tin soldiers—sitting at attention, upright and stiff.

The tall man returned. "Okay, now that we're all here, let's head to the Community Room to get things started." He folded his hands.

Everyone stood but waited for someone to volunteer to go first. The room was empty except for a semi-circle of metal folding chairs. A few worn posters hung on one wall.

I rubbed my ice-cold hands together. Cesar reached for the closest one and cupped it in his; I smiled gratefully.

The participants looked at one another as though sizing each other up. The tall man from earlier, along with a stocky companion, entered the room.

"Hi, I'm Dean. A counselor here. This is John, my colleague," the tall man said. John gave a wave; his pepper-gray pigtail flopped. Dean walked around the circle, handing us a sheet of paper. "This is your schedule for the week. Each of you has been assigned to a counselor."

The schedule was jam-packed, starting early each morning and ending late. There were group meetings, couple therapy sessions, and individual counseling appointments.

I stifled a yawn. All of this was familiar after working the two stints at mental health facilities. I studied my fellow group members. The women looked wide-eyed as though stunned to find themselves at this clinic and in a troubled marriage. The men's faces were harder to read. Cesar's was inscrutable.

With a start, I realized the meeting had ended. "What are we supposed to do?" I asked Cesar.

He glanced at the handout. "According to this, we have counseling first."

Just then, a slender, dark-haired man approached. "Hi, I'm Chuck, your counselor." He led us to a small office that had a distinctly masculine air. A pair of Japanese-styled swords hung on one of the dark green walls. In front of the window was an oversized wooden desk topped with a marble nameplate. I was taken aback to see I had more clinical training than he.

"Make yourselves comfortable." He pointed towards the two wingback chairs. "Why don't you tell me what brings you here."

Cesar peered at me.

"Do you want to begin?" I asked my husband.

"No, go ahead. This is your deal." Cesar stared off.

"Cesar has a sexual addiction." I swallowed hard. "I learned of it a few weeks ago when someone contacted me. She told me they'd been dating."

Chuck turned to Cesar. "Is that about the gist of it?"

"Yeah, it's true." Cesar stared at the floor.

I turned in his direction, puzzled. *What's going on? He wasn't like this with the last therapist.* The room's stillness stretched until I couldn't stand it. "We saw a counselor who specialized in sexual addiction. She recommended residential or inpatient treatment. But we're moving to Mexico and only have time for this."

Chuck didn't react. "Okay. So, why don't we do this." He looked at both of us. "I'll meet with Cesar for an hour, then with you, Kerry. We'll get back together after that to discuss a treatment plan. I should have a better sense of what you're dealing with by then." Chuck swiveled towards me. "Do you mind heading to the waiting room?"

I stood, aware both men were watching, and left.

A few other women were in the lobby. The twenty-something wept into a tissue. I sat in the corner and read.

Cesar touched my shoulder, startling me. "It's your turn to see Chuck," he said. "I'll be attending a men's group but will see you here in an hour." His face was blank.

I found Chuck at his desk. "Come in and make yourself comfortable. I'll be with you in a moment," he said.

I sat down, aware I was alone with a man. Since learning of Cesar's affair, I'd avoided the opposite sex. Something that once had been innocuous now seemed dangerous.

Chuck sat down to join me. "So, why don't you tell me about yourself." For the next hour, he asked questions about my childhood and my marriage to Brad.

"Let me give you this short survey. Answer it in terms of your relationship with Brad, not Cesar." He asked a series of questions. "Would you be surprised to hear Brad might have had problems with intimacy?" he asked. "That's not surprising given you've married Cesar. Sex addiction is often an intimacy issue." I stared. He continued, "I'm not saying Brad had an addiction, just that he struggled to be vulnerable."

The rest of the day stayed busy. The program's focus surprised me. It described sexual addiction as an attack on the partner's self-worth. Children often tattle, hoping an adult will take their side. Did Cesar think I chose this program so he'd get scolded?

As we walked to the car in the dark, I bit my lip nervously. "How are you doing?" I asked.

"It's a lot to take in." He rubbed his temples. "My head is aching from all the information."

I blew out a long breath. "Do you want me to massage your shoulders once we get back to the room?"

"No, that's okay, but thanks."

That night I showered and got ready for bed while Cesar worked on an assignment. Later he snuggled close. "Love you, Gorgeous," he whispered, his voice soft.

I surveyed his face. His eyes shone like two black marbles. "You doing okay? Today was pretty intense."

He closed his eyes. "Yeah, it was. Some of the other stories I heard. Wow..." He shuddered. "Kerry, I'm sorry. I know saying that doesn't count for much. But for what's worth, I'm really sorry."

I leaned to kiss him. He furrowed his brow and hugged me tighter.

For the next two days, we attended group meetings and a combination of individual and couple therapy sessions.

Chuck asked me to write a letter to my childhood abuser. "Once you're done, I want you to beat the couch with that toy bat and to scream as loud as you want." He pointed to a children's toy that leaned against the office wall. "Imagine you're talking to the man who raped you." Then he left the room.

This once-popular psychological technique had fallen out of favor for fueling rather than dissipating emotion. I considered mentioning this but remembered I was the patient, not the expert. *Did I say something that warranted this exercise, or did Chuck use it with every sexual abuse victim?*

With the letter finished, I swung the bat.

"Bastard, you bastard!" I said, feeling silly. I did it again, this time louder, "You motherfucker!" I flopped into the seat, embarrassed.

In the filtered sunlight, dust floated about; distant memories joined them to hover. I saw myself as a little girl trying to survive years of abuse. To have found and then lost Brad, the one person who had truly loved me. Now my fairytale romance to Cesar had been a ruse. Tears streamed down my cheeks.

In between sessions, an older attendee stopped me. "Can I give you a piece of advice?" She leaned until her graying hair brushed mine. "This isn't my first go around."

"Okay..." I said cautiously.

She bent closer. "Whatever you do, keep your finances separate from your husband's." She glowered. "Be smart. Don't trust him."

With raised eyebrows, I forced a smile, "Okay, thanks for advice," and I swallowed hard. This warning had come too late. I'd already made Cesar partner and vice president of the new Mexican company I'd funded. *Cesar would never betray me like that*, I thought as I patted her arm. "Truly, I'll remember this."

Our three-day stay flew by.

Cesar and I entered Chuck's office for our last session.

"Cesar, you'll take a polygraph test to see if you've been telling the truth," Chuck announced.

Cesar's eyes widened.

"Kerry, you and I will come up with the questions to determine the extent of his acting out and to verify that he's been honest this week," he said. "So, what do you think should be included?"

I blinked. *What did Chuck say? Put Cesar on the spot?* A cold sweat broke across my forehead. I'd been too terrified to confront my abuser, yet I was supposed to do so with Cesar? The incident of the smashed phone flashed through my mind. Did Chuck forget I'd have to go home with him? The second hand on the far wall clock slowed. I cleared my throat. "W-w-what do you want me to ask?" I stammered.

"Keep the number of questions to about five and present them in a true or false format," Chuck said. "Let's focus on since you found out about the cheating. Something like, 'Since getting caught, have you, Cesar, texted, spoken to, or seen any other woman sexually or intending to solicit sex beside Kerry?'" Chuck grabbed a pen and notepad from the table and scribbled.

"Yeah, that's a good one." I tried to swallow but couldn't find enough moisture in my parched mouth. With a glance in Cesar's direction, I said, "Shouldn't he leave the room?"

"No, it's best Cesar hears them now," Chuck said.

I squirmed. "Doesn't that confound the results?" Before he could answer, I mumbled, "I haven't had time to prepare for this."

"That's okay. I'm here to help you." Chuck spoke in a low voice.

"I wished I'd more warning. It's awfully hard to do this on the spot." I shot Cesar another look before I stared hard at Chuck. *Doesn't he know this puts me in a dangerous position?*

Since we'd returned from the honeymoon, Cesar had changed. It was as if a hidden frightening potential for rage had been revealed. He was like a toy, wound tight and ready to spring into action.

"We'll come up with them together." Chuck crafted several more. "Okay, I think we have five good ones." He tapped a pen on the pad. "Let's see what you think."

I gave Chuck a long look while he reviewed the list. Each question pertained to Cesar's activities over the past few weeks. None inquired about the range of his sexual behavior or whether he'd put me at risk.

Cesar stared transfixed at the floor in front of him. His face frozen.

My heart raced as I scanned the room for some means of escape.

"Okay, Cesar, now if you'll follow me. It's time to do the testing." Without a word, the two men left.

The only sound in the room was a faint ticking of the clock. *What happens if Cesar fails? Or if he's furious?* I twisted my hands.

Tick, tock, tick, tock... The clock grew louder. Five minutes passed. Then ten. Both men returned fifteen minutes later. The pressure in the room built.

"Let's not keep the two of you in suspense," Chuck said. "Cesar? You passed."

Cesar dropped his head to sob.

"I'm sure it's a relief to get this out of the way."

Cesar nodded.

"I recommend regular polygraphs every three months. Once things are better, you can do them every six months. Down the road, they'll become an annual event." Chuck paused. "It'll keep you accountable, Cesar. And Kerry? It's the only way to know he's telling the truth."

Four times a year? From Mexico? I opened my mouth, speechless. *We can't afford this.*

"There's one more thing." Chuck turned to me. "Kerry, what's your plan if you learn Cesar's been back in touch with a woman?"

I looked down, unsure what to say.

"You're going to need a plan of action. It will reveal a lot about you—if you're strong or a pushover."

My head snapped up.

"So, Kerry, what kind of woman are you? You're obviously smart and attractive. Do you have enough self-worth to set limits?" Chuck's gaze burned through me like two laser beams.

"Yeah, I need to set some boundaries, like leaving if he acts out again," I heard myself say. *Could I?* I dragged my sweaty palms across my slacks.

"Good," Chuck said. "This is just a start. You only know the tip of Cesar's problem. You need to be prepared." I openly stared. *Nah, that can't be right.*

Chuck faced Cesar. "Why don't you share the safeguards you're going to use as motivation." I sat upright, curious.

Cesar glanced down, then at me. "I've created a list of consequences. So, I'm going to wear a rubber wristband and snap it any time I look at a woman," he said. "If I contact someone, then I've committed to telling my mother I'm a sex addict."

Chuck pressed his lips together. "I'm not sure about that last one."

Cesar turned a beet red and burst into tears.

"Oh, that'll be tough to do, Chuck. Believe me," I jumped in to say. "Telling Cesar's mom will break her heart."

Cesar nodded vigorously.

"Well..." Chuck blew out a breath. "As long as you two agree on this one," he said. "Cesar, I strongly recommend you call in to the men's group here. And, Kerry, we don't have anything like that for you, but there are several good online women's groups. Be sure to find something that fits your needs." He considered us for a second. "I'm here for phone sessions. You have a long way to go, but you've started the journey. I know you have a few more meetings to attend today, but I want to wish you both the best of luck."

Cesar and I stood and shook Chuck's hand.

On the walk back to the lobby, my head pounded as Chuck's comment about not being a weak woman replayed.

The large waiting area was empty. Cesar checked the schedule. "I'll see you in two hours. Let's meet here." He turned and left.

My last meeting was back in the large conference room—this time, the semi-circle comprised us women. The twenty-something was crying again. The woman next to me whispered, "Her husband failed his polygraph. During an hour-long full disclosure, she found out he's been up to a lot more than she knew."

"Oh?" The young woman reminded me of the rape victims I used to counsel. Traumatized and tear-stained, the simplest question left them bewildered. *Where was her advocate? Or mine?*

Despite the meeting's start, I kept thinking about the other woman. Why did her husband have an extensive interview, and we didn't? Cesar hasn't been asked in-depth questions. Then, something new occurred to me. *For the past few weeks, he's been on his best behavior; passing the lie-detector test would have been easy.* My stomach lurched.

There was a spring in Cesar's step like an enormous weight had been lifted on the walk to the car later that afternoon. His good mood was back.

I trudged, shaken by what I'd learned. The entire program's focus had been on managing his problem, not on helping me. I was leaving in no better shape than I had arrived. *At least that other woman knows the truth*, I thought.

We were leaving for Mexico in two days. *What have I gotten myself into?* I wondered.

14

ANOTHER BEGINNING

"It's the simple things in your life that make up the bulk of it. The mundane is where we live and we end up missing most of it. We find it again in the silence and in attention of everyday life."
—Eric Overby, *17: Haiku Poem*

Mid-October 2017

FROM THE LIVING room, I heard Cesar retching—his third time this morning. We had gotten home late yesterday afternoon and met Devon for dinner. Cesar must have eaten something bad at the Chinese buffet.

I walked into the bedroom to see how he was doing.

The wire bedsprings jiggled as he crawled in. His face was pale, and his forehead was covered in sweat. He clutched the blanket, shivering.

I brushed the hair from his eyes. His skin was feverishly hot. "Can I get you anything?"

"No. Thanks, though," he mumbled, half-asleep. His eyelids fluttered shut.

On yesterday's flight home, Cesar spoke about his experience at the treatment center. One of the attendees, a cocky guy, had told the other men that he wasn't a sex pervert like the rest of them. Cesar had spoken fast and waved his hands.

"The man's wife had threatened to take the kids if he didn't attend," Cesar explained. He sighed. "And he came with a new girlfriend—a much younger thing." He spat out that last phrase. "You should have seen the way he looked at us like he was better." Cesar snorted. "There was his wife, trying to keep the family together, off to the side, bawling." Cesar stared off as though lost in thought. "A counselor asked if this was his first affair. The guy considered his answer and then admitted he'd cheated before. That girl was just one in a long line of women," he said. "Better than the rest of us... right." He growled the last word. "I'm sorry, Gorgeous. Really sorry. I didn't know how bad I'd hurt you." He squeezed my hand. "I'm glad we're working on this." He gazed tenderly.

"It's just a start, Cesar," I said.

"Yeah, I know." A second passed. "I've already been searching for a counselor, someone who would be a good fit." He turned towards me. "Would you help with that?"

"Yeah, sure. Of course," I said, overly eager, then checked myself. *This is his job. It's his recovery, not mine.* "I'm glad we caught this now and not years down the road."

"Yeah, me too." He sighed, and, for a long second, we held each other's eyes.

That night I wrapped my arms and legs about Cesar's waist to envelop him. As our bodies rocked with his thrusts, a need to meld as one consumed me. I wanted to heal him. To heal us. To heal me. When he came, I whispered, "I love you, Cesar. I love you so much."

He pulled me close. "Love you more, Gorgeous. I love you more than you know." His voice was drowsy.

For a long moment, I listened to him breathe. *We can do this. We're different. Cesar loves me. We'll be one of the lucky few who will beat this addiction.* Cesar woke, sick.

I rolled out of bed with a sigh. *Our stuff isn't going to pack itself.* Ten empty suitcases waited against the bedroom wall. Instead of getting started, I walked over to look out the bedroom window. Feeble sunlight filtered in. A grocery bag floated across the rental's parking lot. It dipped and twisted in the wind. *Another dreary day.*

I tiptoed past the bed, where Cesar snored and grabbed an armload of clothes. While rolling our undergarments into tight balls, I contemplated the state of our marriage. No one in my immediate family knew about the affairs—not my mom, sisters, or sons. There would be questions—ones I wasn't ready to answer. And outrage too. They'd want me to make a decision, and if I stayed, I'd probably lose the little family support that remained.

Cesar had lied about it being his first affair. Most of the time, he seemed desperate to get better. He'd told me he'd shared with a previous wife that he was in trouble. She'd laughed and said there was no such thing as sex addiction; it was just a made-up excuse. He grabbed my hand. "Thanks, Kerry, for believing me."

Our lovemaking last night had been filled with tenderness. Was this a sign of progress? I'd made it my career to help others change. *Can we overcome this?*

My head throbbed.

Cesar blinked sleepily. "Gorgeous? You doing okay?"

"Yeah, I'm fine. Just packing."

"I'm sorry I'm not helping." His voice was raspy.

"Get some sleep; I got this. Tomorrow is a bigger day," I said with a quick look at the ten suitcases.

It was early evening when the oversized bags sat in the rental's kitchen, their seams bulging. I turned on the corner lamp before heading for an ice pack.

Everything ached—my back, my stomach, my knees, but especially my heart. *I'm grieving.*

When couples come together, they create a secret world constructed of the private things said. The inside jokes. The words of affection. And the stories that are told. Even the way love is made—the where, when, and how.

He'd spent our first holiday weekend with Maria. That morning, he'd kissed me goodbye despite my pleas. He'd left, not for a business trip like he said, but on a getaway with her. How often had they fucked? Did he call her "Gorgeous," too?

Engraving his wedding gift had been difficult. I had to find someone with the right equipment to inscribe the stainless-steel bracelet with the words, "For Forever." He had put it on Susan's wrist.

Tears leaked out of the corners of my eyes. I turned on the TV but only found game shows and reruns and turned it back off. In its fading glow, the room grew darker.

For the past several weeks, Cesar and I had been together nearly every second of every day. At first, his proximity was reassuring. I knew he was with me and not with someone else. But his booming voice began to hurt my ears. He interrupted and liked to debate. Now there was no respite from him. I'd sacrificed solitude for safety.

For the first time since the morning on the beach after receiving Susan's letter, I was alone. *Why am I staying?* I could get a divorce, maybe even an annulment. Commitments, marriage being the most solemn, were everything to me. Being a person of integrity defined me—not just as someone of faith, though it pleased God. It was who I was—a person of my word. I'd made a promise to Cesar—to love him through good times and bad. To some, this might be a weakness, but to me, it was strength. I could be counted on.

Did I still love him?

From where I sat on the couch, I could see him sleeping. Soft snores emanated from the bedroom.

Despite the pain he'd caused, yes, I did love him, with such longing that sometimes it made me gasp. Not so much sexually, although I desired him. This feeling went deeper. More primal. Once in a while, there'd be a flash of a scared little boy who desperately wanted to be cherished. It was him I loved and him I hoped to save.

Though it was still early evening, I crawled in beside Cesar. For a long while, I listened to him sleep.

The room was pitch black when the alarm sounded early the next morning. I rolled over to see how he was doing. Already awake, his eyes met mine.

"How are you?" I asked.

"Better," he said.

"You look better. Ready to do this?"

"Yeah, I am. Are you?" A start of an excited smile turned his mouth. His eyes twinkled.

"I think so," I said with less enthusiasm.

"Let's pray. Would that be okay, Gorgeous?"

I nodded gratefully. Holding my hand, he asked for God's protection.

Our jet circled over Mexico's brilliant green coastline and the Caribbean's bright turquoise blues late that afternoon. The jungle sharpened into individual trees as the plane dropped lower. Another round of announcements in Spanish blared across the jet's interior.

Cesar shook my shoulder, grinning ear-to-ear. "This is it, Gorgeous! We're arriving in Mexico!" His knee bounced like a jackhammer. "We're really doing this!"

I gave him a half-hearted smile. Though I'd suggested this move, since learning of his affairs, life had become drab.

After immigration and customs, we picked up the van. Soon stacks of suitcases filled its cargo area. I sat scrunched, my knees against the dashboard, and turned to look at all that I owned.

It was dusk when we pulled away from the airport. So close to the equator, the sun set early. We settled in at a nearby hotel. The next morning, we headed for our new home, a condo on the outskirts of Playa del Carmen. Colorful stores and resorts lined both sides of the highway. Trees aflame with bright red flowers dotted the center median. Drivers zipped around on an imaginary third lane. Teenage boys on bike carts sold snow cones and snacks, and tired workers stood by the roadside waiting for a *colectivo*, Spanish for a large transportation van. I had entered a strange world.

"Hey, what do you think of going shopping for a mattress and some furniture today?" I said. "We'll need something to sleep on."

"That's what I was thinking," Cesar said. He turned into a gated subdivision and introduced himself in Spanish to the attendant. The man gave us entrance. We crawled through a quiet neighborhood of square cement-block houses and pulled in front of a large building. Cesar turned off the ignition, but neither of us moved. The only sound was the van's engine ticking as it cooled.

Cesar turned. "Can you believe it? We're here." My smile matched his.

Our empty fourth-floor penthouse smelled stale. Cesar opened several windows while I rushed to the rooftop. Once at the railing, I looked out. In the distance, the ocean shimmered streaks of blue and silver. A gentle breeze stirred my hair and made the overhead awning snap.

Cesar joined me. "This is amazing!" I said. And for a moment, we stood in awed silence.

For the next few days, we visited several furniture stores and ordered furnishings. While we waited for their deliveries, we went to the beach, swam in the condo's pool, dined out on Mexican fare, and made love often.

One night we watched the stars from the penthouse roof. Cesar cradled my head while we stared up at the nighttime sky. The vastness of the stars made my vision swim. A bright light shot across the sky.

"I just saw a shooting star!" I pointed.

"Where?" Cesar asked. We rushed to the rooftop's edge.

"Over there!"

Just then, another streaked past.

"I saw one too!" Cesar's smile lit his eyes, and his face softened. "I love you, Gorgeous." He squeezed me to his chest.

I stood on tiptoes to kiss his mouth. "I love you too," I whispered. And briefly, the pain was left behind.

15

EVERYTHING'S NEW

"A storyteller makes up things to help other people; a liar makes up things to help himself."
—Daniel Wallace, *The Kings and Queens of Roam*

Early November 2017

THE METAL CHAIR cut into the back of my legs. Over an hour ago, Cesar and I arrived at the bank to open a business account. He looked at his watch and then at the young manager who typed at her computer. I nodded and willed her to work faster. He huffed in frustration.

The manager swiveled. "What is your street address?" she asked Cesar in Spanish.

"Please talk to my wife. She's the company's head," Cesar said for the third time. She stared at him, blank-faced, and asked him another question.

When it came to running a business, there was little resemblance between the US and Mexico. Everywhere we went, we had to complete handwritten applications to buy the simplest of things, even a toaster. Our days were spent going store to store, opening accounts, purchasing supplies, and signing up for memberships. I had to go as the company's president, and Cesar accompanied me as the interpreter.

Another form rolled off the old-fashioned printer that sat beside the manager's desk. She pushed the page in front of me, pointing at the bottom line. "Complete name and signature. Sign like your passport," she said in broken English. This request was one of many oddities here.

Cesar's knee bounced in time with my tapping foot. We exchanged another look.

"Are we close to being finished?" Cesar asked.

"Almost," the manager replied. "Hmm... fifteen minutes?" She didn't bother to look up.

With a loud exhale, Cesar rolled his eyes. My stomach growled. Since leaving the house early that morning, we hadn't stopped to eat. Another form was slid in front of me. "Okay, last signature," the manager said. "Debit cards ready in two weeks."

Cesar's mouth fell open. "We need them now."

"I'm sorry, not possible." A look of impatience crossed her face. "Two weeks. Come back in two weeks," she said in English.

We both stood to leave.

"Can we schedule an appointment to pick them up?" Cesar asked, irritated.

"No. Call first to see if the cards ready," she replied.

"You gotta be kidding me." Cesar scowled. "I can't make an appointment because you don't know when the cards will be ready, but I'm to check every day." He sputtered, "Unbelievable."

With my head low, I rocked back and forth, uncomfortably. For the past few days, the smallest thing seemed to set Cesar off.

"I'm sorry. Best I can do," she said in a monotone voice; she turned, ending the conversation.

I'd mistakenly thought *mañana* meant things here were laid-back, but it described how things were done—at a slow pace and not on my timeline. There was a week's wait for internet and phone service; deliveries occurred any time of the day but required a signature, and a mandatory in-home interview was necessary to open a bank account. Every task was complicated by unpredictable schedules and complex bureaucracy.

Cesar stormed out. "Can you believe it? Two weeks. Two more weeks before we get a debit card!" Then he growled, "What a bitch!"

I stared, transfixed.

"Let's grab lunch, Gorgeous. I'm starving," he said, changing the subject, and reached for my hand before crossing the street. I kneaded my throbbing jaw with a reminder that my oldest son, Cameron, would be arriving in a few days.

We got home as the sun set.

Dropping my purse on the table, I grabbed my cell phone. "I'm heading upstairs to the rooftop. It's almost time for group," I called out.

Cesar answered from the back bedroom closet, "Sure, no problem."

Since the intensive treatment program, Cesar attended Chuck's call-in group, and I'd found a twelve-week program for partners of sex addicts. Each week, I met with the coach and two other women.

A breeze blew in from off the ocean as the last of the fiery-red sun disappeared behind the jungle greenery. The patio lighting clicked on to cast a yellow glow. I dialed in.

"Kerry, I'm so glad you could join us. Okay, ladies, time for check-in," the coach said in her lively, high-pitched voice.

Katie, a young member, spoke first. "I'm having the same issue as last week." She exhaled loudly. "My husband still locks himself in our spare bedroom. I know what he's up to—the same things he's been doing for the past fifteen years." Katie trailed off. "I've had it... yet I stay. What's wrong with me?"

I squirmed. *Is this going to be me someday?*

"You're talking about it—that's the good thing," the coach said. "It's self-care, and that's the start of making a change." She paused. "Have any of you heard the term fear-bonded? It's a type of trauma bond."

There was a collective no.

"Fear connects you to your partner. It creates a deep dependency, similar to an addiction," she said. "I'm going to email you all a handout to review for next week."

I listened to the next member while I rubbed my pounding head.

"Kerry, how's it going?" the coach asked.

"Things with the business have been busier than I'd expected. Every day we hit some new snag, but otherwise, Cesar and I are doing okay," I said. "He's attending a men's group and went to a 12-Step meeting last week."

There was an awkward pause.

"That's good, Kerry, really good. Remember, this is a marathon, though, not a sprint. It's gonna take time to know if he's in recovery." Then she addressed the group. "Don't forget to pay attention to your gut. Intuition is your first line of defense. It picks up on cues faster than your mind," she said. "And ladies, make self-care a priority. You are important, so be sure to schedule some time for you too!"

I sat for a few moments thinking through what was said during the call. How did I end up in a group of women married to sex addicts? My lip curled. "Sex addicts" conjured images of strangers fucking in back alleys. With a sudden weariness, I headed downstairs.

Cesar was in the living room with his head bent over his phone. A stream of videos played on the TV like a screen saver. Without looking up, he asked, "How did it go, Gorgeous?"

"Fine. You know, the usual."

"That's good." Neither of us pressed each other for too much information about therapy sessions.

"What are you doing?"

He glanced up, his cheeks flushed. "Well, I'm embarrassed to say." He swiped at his phone's screen. "I'm cleaning my text messages and deleting the names of female contacts."

"Oh?" I looked up in surprise. He'd mentioned a few women, but I'd assumed they were friends. The room suddenly felt too small. I needed space—breathing room from something intimate yet grotesque—and took a seat at the kitchen table far away from the women's names and faces.

"Yeah, I'm shocked to see how many there are." Cesar continued to tap at his device.

I tensed. "How many, do you think?" I said casually as possible.

"Forty, maybe fifty?" he mumbled. "A lot."

I swayed. "That is a lot," I whispered.

Cesar looked up to stare. "Yeah, I know." His cheeks turned a dull red. "I really had no idea it was this many. I mean, I knew there were quite a few." He spoke in a rush. "Too many to keep straight."

"Well, it's good that you're doing this." I smiled to hide my horror.

"Since we both have new numbers, I figured it was a good time." He bent back over his phone.

I staggered to the bedroom. *Forty to fifty women... He'd been sexting forty to fifty women?* I fell face-first onto the bed. Chuck had warned we only knew a tiny portion of Cesar's addiction. I thought he'd gotten it wrong. Chuck didn't know us or even Cesar, yet the disclosures continued to trickle out. Suddenly sick, I rushed to the toilet.

A few days later, Cesar and I stood outside the airport's terminal. Cameron's flight had arrived. Since he moved to Texas a few years ago, I mostly saw him during the holidays. The last time had been at the wedding celebration.

The setting sun had turned the sky a midnight blue, tinged in swirls of reddish pink. An ocean wind cooled my sticky skin. Thanksgiving was two weeks away, yet the tropical weather stayed blistering hot.

Cesar nudged me. "I think I see him!" He pointed down the concrete corridor of the airport's exit.

A slender man hauling a large suitcase sauntered towards us. His head weaved in a familiar way. I grinned as he drew closer.

"Hey!" Cameron leaned forward to give me a quick one-armed hug. A flash of his earthy scent made me want to hug him again. To cling to him. Here was someone safe. Someone I could trust. The words of what I'd been going through sat on my tongue. *You can't,* I reminded myself. *He's not your therapist.* "It's so good to see you!"

Cameron turned to give Cesar a friendly smile. They were still strangers, though they'd met at the wedding. Cesar leaned over to pat Cameron's shoulder.

For the next few days, I showed Cameron around while he caught us up on his new job and what it was like living with his brother, my youngest son, Kellin.

While we lay on the beach, Cameron asked, "How about you, Mom? How are you doing?"

"I'm doing good," I said with my best fake smile.

He nodded. "I'm glad." He took another sip of a daiquiri. "I could get used to this." He glanced across the beach filled with women clad in bikinis.

I snorted. "I'll bet."

He smirked.

Does my husband feel the same way? I wondered. I gazed at the semi-nude bodies lounging around us and then at Cesar. Cesar had his eyes shut as though dozing. It was one thing for a single, twenty-something man to admire a woman, but quite something else when it was a spouse.

Since leaving the treatment center, Cesar snapped his wristband several times a week and often asked to switch restaurant seats. Was he in recovery? My coach said it would take time to tell.

Cameron's visit ended too soon. On the drive to the airport, I listened from the backseat to the two men chat like old friends while the resorts zipped past. One of the names looked familiar. Cesar may have mentioned it as a place where he and Maria had stayed. A short time after we'd started dating, Cesar had called to remind me he'd be out of town for a family wedding, but he had gone with Maria, not with his mother as he had said. Just before he hung up that night, he asked if we could go steady. I had laughed at his use of the old-fashioned word and then said, "Yes."

Had Cesar noticed? From the rearview mirror, I could see him laughing at something Cameron had said. Sickened by the memory, I turned back towards the window.

16

RELAPSE

"One believed what one was told to believe, what it made sense to believe.
Unless one was a foreigner, of course, or a philosopher."
—Iain M. Banks, *Inversions*

Late November 2017

"IT'S ALMOST TIME to call Chuck," I said.

"We can take it from here." Cesar pulled into a small downtown parking lot.

"Ready?"

He nodded. A muscle in his jawline twitched.

In dead silence, we waited for Chuck to answer.

Cesar had relapsed.

Chuck had tried to warn me this might happen, but I didn't believe him. We'd been doing great, so I thought. We'd been attending Sunday church, taking long walks, cuddling while watching movies, and talking for hours about one subject after another.

It had been Cesar's idea to begin each day with devotions. He showed me the description of a book he'd found written especially for couples, and we ordered a copy. Since its arrival, we hadn't missed taking turns reading one aloud each day. Cesar would find the page he'd bookmarked to start us off and then end the time in prayer.

What if Chuck thinks I should leave?

No, I counted on Cesar. I needed him—loved him.

After Cameron's visit, we had jumped back into getting the rental business off the ground. Nothing was going as planned. Labor shortages and a backlog of deliveries had pushed the schedule months behind, forcing us to cancel guests' reservations for Christmas. Cesar grew short-tempered, and I, homesick. Thinking we needed a break, I made reservations at a nearby resort.

The day before Thanksgiving, we checked into a small hotel room with a view of the ocean. That afternoon we swam and then dressed for dinner. Cesar looked as exhausted as I felt.

As we got around the next morning, Cesar said, "Did you notice this place has sailboats for rent?"

"I know!" I said with a warm smile.

"Do you want to go with me?"

"Nah, I'm too tired. I think I'll hang out at the pool," I said. "But don't let that stop you."

Grinning ear-to-ear, he bounded off, returning an hour later dripping wet and happy. "Hey, let's head to the room," he said. "Maybe for a drink?"

Following Cesar out onto the balcony, I sat down with a glass of wine and propped my feet against the railing. Out beyond, the ocean waves surged; its rhythm was slow and tranquil. "Just what I needed," I said with a sigh.

In the chair beside me, Cesar jiggled one leg and then the other. He slapped his thighs and stood. "Hey, I feel sticky. I'm going to take a shower." He headed inside.

On the patio table lay Cesar's cell phone. The shower spigot turned on. I glanced behind—the bedroom was empty—and reached for it but stopped mid-way. *What's going on with me? I don't do stuff like this. Where is this coming from?* I wavered and then remembered seeing the resort sign where he and Maria had stayed. As I finished grabbing it, I reminded myself, *There's no going back.*

After fumbling with the passcode, the home screen filled with colorful apps. I stared at it for a moment before opening his emails, then my stomach did a somersault. Among the usual junk was a letter to Maria, sent the day Cameron left.

Just then, the shower shut off, and a towel snapped.

I whipped around. The main room was still empty. After forwarding myself a copy, I returned the phone where I'd found it. My heart pounded with such force it threatened to burst out of my chest. With a deep breath, I gazed out at the water. The glass of wine jostled in my shaking hand.

Cesar's voice came from behind. "Whew, I feel better." He stepped onto the patio, dressed in shorts and holding a beer.

"That's good," I said. The calmness of my voice hid my nervousness. "It's such a nice evening."

He sat down, staring out at the water, and took a swig. "What an incredible view. Thanks, Gorgeous, for planning this."

I sat on my hands to hide their trembling. "You're welcome."

For a moment, no one spoke.

Standing, I flashed Cesar a smile. "Now it's my turn to use the bathroom." Cesar's face tightened as I reached for my phone.

Once in the other room, I went limp with a loud exhale. With only a few minutes to spare, I ran Cesar's message written in Spanish through a translator. It read:

Dear Maria,

I drove past the resort where you and I stayed and remembered our trip with fondness. I'm unhappy in a prison of a sort. I wanted you to know that I think about you often.

Hugs and kisses,

Cesar

The temperature dropped to freezing in the small muggy room, and my teeth chattered.

"You okay, Gorgeous?" Cesar asked. His voice was muffled through the closed door.

"Yeah," I answered. My fingers shook as I typed a short message to Chuck, our couple's counselor. "We need a session," I wrote to him. Along with the brief note, I attached Cesar's original letter and its translation. Once it was sent, I flushed the empty toilet and washed my clean hands before rejoining him.

"Everything all right?" he asked with an extra-long stare.

"Yeah." I smiled. "Why wouldn't it be?"

"I don't know. You were gone a long time."

"How could everything not be good in a place like this?" I raised my glass in his direction before taking a sip while my mind continued to race.

On the day we drove Cameron to the airport, Cesar had thought of Maria. *He considers our marriage a prison?* I thought about our running jokes, how often we lingered over dinner, and played tag in the pool, teasing each other. None of what he'd written made sense.

Unable to reconcile his painful words, they suddenly blinked out of existence like other troubling memories.

I must have been going on six years old when I crept into the bathroom where my mother readied for bed. I needed to confess something. Something bad. Uncle liked to wrap his lean body against the back of mine while we lay on the floor and watched TV. He'd pull me close. Then closer, until the front of his crotch rubbed against the curve of my bum. Though the unwanted sensation was oddly pleasant, I'd go still and pretend it wasn't happening. Maybe he'd stop. Upsetting him was a bad idea.

The nights he babysat were the worst. While feigning sleep, I'd plead with God, "Make him go away, make him go away." Only he didn't, and I wanted to die.

Mom sat down on the toilet lid. "What are you doing up?"

I took a step closer and balled my hands behind my back. With my eyes screwed tight, I blurted, "Uncle's been doing something naughty."

"Shhh..." she'd said. "Go back to bed and put it out of your mind." She gave my shoulder a gentle push towards the door.

In the bedroom's darkness, my little sister's bunkbed wireframe was barely visible above me. "Forget," I whispered and fell asleep. And just like that, those ugly memories were tucked away, out of sight, and forgotten. It wasn't until I turned twelve that I went from not knowing to knowing like a drop cloth lifted to reveal what was hidden beneath.

The next morning, I woke to the sound of room service. Cesar walked in from a jog, looking sweaty, as the wait staff delivered coffee, juice, and a tray of danish rolls.

"Hot out this morning. I'm going to take a quick shower. Shall we eat on the balcony?" he asked.

"Sure." I pulled on a housecoat and poured a cup of coffee. The ocean shimmered with lacy bands of dancing sunlight; its gentle, undulating waves lapped at the sandy shoreline. Cesar placed a large tray of food on the table and sat down.

I watched him take a sip of juice and then looked at the ocean for strength. "Beautiful day."

"It is." He took a bite of food, his eyes darting in my direction. "You've been awfully quiet. Everything okay?"

"Actually, it's not," I said.

"Okay... so now what did I do wrong?"

I ruffled, irritated. Boys said such things, not men. "You emailed Maria and reminisced about staying at that resort we passed. Then you complained our marriage was a prison of sorts."

"That's not what I said," Cesar growled.

"Well, you said something like that. That you were unhappy." I paused. "You told me the purpose of the July Fourth trip was to say goodbye. I guess it wasn't much of a farewell if you're reminiscing about it." With a sudden flash of insight, my eyes widened. "She doesn't know you're married!"

Cesar opened his mouth as if to say something but then closed it.

"She doesn't, does she?" I gave him a probing stare.

Cesar looked down. "No, no, she doesn't know."

I fell backward. "So, you even lied about that."

"I wanted it to be a goodbye," he whined. "But you're right; it wasn't."

"Chuck knows. I sent him a copy of the email, and we have an appointment with him tomorrow." Cesar looked away.

For the rest of the day, we stayed out of each other's way like two wild cats forced to share a cage.

The engine of the vehicle idled while we waited for Chuck to answer.

"Hi, Chuck, this is Kerry. Cesar's with me," I said.

"Hi, guys." Chuck waited for a beat. "Cesar, are you aware Kerry scheduled this phone appointment?" The line crackled with static.

"Yeah, she told me," Cesar said.

"What's going on?" Chuck asked.

Cesar glanced at me. "Well, since Kerry got a hold of you, she should go first."

I shot him a look.

"I'd like to hear your side, Cesar," Chuck said.

"I don't know what to say, except that I messed up."

Chuck's voice broke up over the car's stereo. "It sounds like you messed up. What happened?"

"What did Kerry write?" Cesar asked.

"I want you to tell me the details," Chuck said.

"I emailed an old girlfriend, but I'm sure you already know that," Cesar said. "It was a dumb move; I was upset. Kerry and I had gotten into an argument, so I reached out." His comment reminded me we'd fought that morning about something inconsequential.

"The letter Kerry sent was in Spanish. Care to tell me what it said?"

Cesar scowled.

I twisted my fingers until the joints were a bloodless white.

"Didn't Kerry send you a translation?" Cesar asked.

"Yes, but it doesn't make sense. Something about feeling imprisoned?" Chuck said.

"That's not what it said."

"So, what did it say?"

"I was pissed, okay?" Cesar said.

"It's not okay. You contacted a woman. Someone you've had an affair with—so no, this is not okay." Chuck paused. "Now it becomes an issue for Kerry." His voice changed. "So, Kerry, what are you going to do?"

I twirled towards the dashboard speakers. "What??" I asked. *Where's Cesar's verbal lashing? The pep talk about marital faithfulness?*

"Kerry, have you figured out your new boundaries?" Chuck asked. "Cesar has cheated again. Are there going to be consequences, or are you going to let him get away with this?"

I panicked. *I'm supposed to kick him out? To where and with what money? Can I handle a Mexican business alone?* "Well..." I scrambled for something to say. "I don't know..."

"If you don't take a stand, Cesar will do this again, only worse," Chuck said. "So, what kind of woman are you? Someone who lets him get away with stuff like this, or someone who thinks she deserves better?"

My chest tightened as if in a vice-like grip. "I don't know, Chuck. I know what you want me to say, but I'm not ready." My face burned hot. I could feel Cesar's icy-cold stare as he listened. This man was acting like an adversary, not like my husband. Chuck's bluntness had likely drawn attention to my precarious standing in the marriage.

"Kerry, you're an attractive, smart woman. You have options. You'll find love again," Chuck said.

I stiffened. *It's over?* The back of my head pounded. What if I wasn't so good-looking? What would happen if I got heavier or grew older? How am I supposed to run a business from here? I suddenly felt very alone. "Thanks, Chuck. I'll give what you said a lot of thought."

"Back to the matter at hand. Cesar, contacting Maria was way over the line," Chuck said. "You haven't been in the men's group for the past few weeks. Accountability is essential for sobriety. What's going on?"

Cesar's eyes grew small. "I know, Chuck." His voice dripped with scorn. "I'm having trouble connecting with the other guys. They seem to be really struggling. Not where I'm at."

"That's exactly where you're at, and it's where you need to be," Chuck said. "You've only attended a couple of meetings. It's too soon to make that call. You need to give it more time."

"Okay, I hear you. I'll think about it." Cesar's answer reminded me of something a kid would say after a scolding.

"One more thing," Chuck said. "Did we talk about follow-up polygraph tests?"

"Yes," we both answered.

"Our program recommends one every three months at first. Your last was in early October; that means you're due in a month. Best to get it on the calendar now."

"Okay, Chuck. Thank you." Cesar sounded bored, clearly done with the conversation. "We'll look into that."

"You both have a lot to process. Want to schedule something next week?"

I hesitated, unsure if I could trust Chuck. This appointment had been more contentious than supportive. I bristled, confused. "I'll get back to you," I said.

"Well, let me know," Chuck said.

After the call ended, neither of us moved.

"What do you think, Gorgeous?" Cesar asked.

Looking straight ahead, I said. "I don't know what to think." And then I turned to face him. "I can't believe you contacted her and said those things. Do you regret marrying me?" I watched to see if he was lying.

"I was angry when I wrote that." He shook his head. "I know now I shouldn't have done it," he grumbled. "I'm sorry, Gorgeous." His eyes glistened with unshed tears.

I glared. "You've lied and lied to me. You've even lied to Maria." I exhaled slowly. "I don't know what to believe anymore." The pressure of tears stung my eyes, but I refused to let them fall. "Well, I guess it's time to plan that trip to see your mom." My voice rose. "That was the agreed-upon consequence, right?" We locked eyes in an imaginary stare-down.

Cesar's lips narrowed before his face crumbled in defeat. "Yeah, you're right. I did agree to tell my mom if I got ahold of another woman."

My anger drained. "It's as good a time as any with Christmas a few weeks away. We can use the holidays as an excuse," I added, softening the blow. *Stop rescuing him.*

"I'd like to write Maria a letter," he said, "with your help, of course. I need to tell her I'm married. Would that be okay?"

"Sure," I said. *No! No, I don't want any part of this.* Their affair had stolen something precious from me. From us.

"What do you think?" He handed his phone to me. The device felt oddly heavy in my palm. I wanted to divine its secrets and smash it into pieces.

In English, he'd written:

Dear Maria,

I know now contacting you was a mistake. I'm married. I'm sorry I sent you that letter last week. I've hurt my wife, and I've hurt you. You won't be hearing from me again.

I wish you all the best,
Cesar

I looked up. "It says what it needs to."

"You think?" Cesar bent back over his phone and touched the screen. "Okay, sent." He looked up, all smiles, like a boy making a grand show of returning the money after getting caught pilfering the church's alms box. I recognized the look. It was manipulation mimicking remorse.

A desire to hurt him swelled. "Looks like it's time to make another trip to the treatment center," I said coolly.

"Whatever you think, Gorgeous." His acquiescence had made the problem mine. Another trip would be expensive. Since Cesar had no money of his own and our business wouldn't earn income for several more months, I would have to pay. Yet, skipping the polygraph meant I'd have to take Cesar's word. I gulped at that thought.

"Yeah, we need to go," I said, with a sigh, and pulled out the phone to start making the plans.

17

UNSTEADY

"Anybody who says they are a good liar obviously is not, because any legitimately savvy liar would always insist they're honest about everything."
—Chuck Klosterman

Early December 2017

THE JET CIRCLED over Mexico City's hazy sky. Densely packed buildings divided by meandering roadways clustered inside the mountain range's earthen bowl. I'd met Cesar's mom once before. The tiny woman had welcomed me with a home-cooked meal and a big hug.

Cesar disliked talking about his past. I'd pieced together that his home had been ruled by a violent man, one popular with the ladies.

"We had a hard time keeping help," Cesar said.

"Hmm..." I replied. "I'll bet I know why."

"Why?" He blinked rapidly.

"Because of your dad. When you're poor, it's hard to say no to the boss. Leaving is easier; at least you haven't ruined your reference."

"Ohhh..." Cesar's eyes widened. "I'd finished school when he walked out." He curled his lips as though he'd tasted something bitter. "He said, 'I put two of you through college, now it's your turn to take care of your mother.'" As Cesar said this, he looked through me, caught in the memories, and fell silent.

The trip came together quickly. I added a few days to sightsee before we left for his mother's hometown. Cesar texted *Mamita*, his pet name for her, to let her know we were coming. Nothing was mentioned of the reason for the last-minute visit.

"Oh, Maria's written back." With a grin, he stuck his phone in my direction.

My dearest Cesar,
You're married?!?
All my love,
Maria

Confused, I re-read it several times. *My dearest Cesar? All my love?* Was she trying to hurt my feelings or stroke his ego? *Maybe both.* Cesar's stare grew heavy. I exhaled loudly. "Well, at least she knows," I said.

He slid the phone into his pocket with a smile.

Relapse was an expected part of an addict's recovery; it meant a course correction was indicated. Chuck was probably right: Cesar needed to be back in group, but I couldn't enforce it.

And I thought we'd been doing well. This wasn't just a slip. It was a betrayal, though it hadn't hurt as bad as the first time. A fragile callus had started to grow over my heart. His letter had scrubbed it raw like sandpaper on bare wood.

Isn't marriage supposed to be a lifelong commitment? We'd vowed, "until death do us part." How much is too much? The closer I approached what I thought were well-defined limits the fuzzier they appeared. I still loved Cesar, not with the same butterfly feelings, but for his potential. Was I weak to hold out hope? *Leaving isn't simple despite what Chuck may think.* I wouldn't walk out on one of my kids. Why would I walk out on a spouse?

As the jet neared the airport, turbulence shook my seat. Another round of announcements crackled over the loudspeakers. This time I recognized a few words. Cesar leaned across to peer out the window.

"Look, Gorgeous! We're almost there!" He shook my arm with excitement. "I can't wait for us to visit my family. You know, you're the first woman I've taken to meet them." I returned his infectious grin, though puzzled by his comment since I'd met his mother and sister before.

We exited onto a crowded concourse filled with parents tugging along tired children. I lagged, breathless from the city's thin air.

Cesar glanced back. "You doing okay?"

"Slow down. Just a bit." I readjusted my grip on the carry-on luggage.

"Here, let me help you with that," he said and grabbed my suitcase's handle.

"No, it's okay. You already have too much between the backpack and your carry-on." I reached to take it back.

"I'm okay!" Cesar whipped his head back and forth. Too tired to complain, I trudged behind.

The taxi pulled over at a small boutique hotel. A doorman rushed forward. His pressed black slacks and bright red jacket with polished gold buttons reminded me of a footman out of a fairytale. Rows of flower gardens graced the fronts of intricately decorated buildings. Cesar beamed as I swirled to take in the panoramic view.

The hotel's interior was just as magnificent. Light from the story-high leaded windows made the carpets glow a blood red, and the winding staircase's mahogany balustrade warmed to dark chocolate. While Cesar tipped the bellhop, I ran to the nearest window. Pink rose gardens separated the tall trees that lined both sides of the city street.

I heard Cesar move about the room, hanging up a few of his clothes.

"It's so beautiful!" I said. "Not at all what I expected."

He joined me. "Mamita and I toured the city a couple of years ago. It was pretty incredible," he said. "Would you like to do that?"

My face fell. The walk through the airport had been difficult. There was no way I could manage a day of sightseeing. "Maybe another time." I smiled, hoping to curb the sting.

Cesar's face hardened. "Sure, let's do it some other time." He returned to unpacking.

I watched him for a moment. When we first met, he said he understood my health issues but lately chafed at living within their limitations. *Does he regret marrying me?* He said so in his letter to Maria. Brad's love had matured; was I naïve to believe Cesar's would, too?

"I hoped we'd visit Chapultepec Castle and the statue of the Angel of Independence," I said, hoping this sounded like a peace offering.

Keeping his back to me, he said in a flat voice, "Sure, sounds good."

Intimacy was discovered in the small things, like knowing how Cesar brushed his hair or hung his slacks. Learning about his choice in music, how he liked his eggs cooked, and the sounds he made when sleeping. I looked back out the window and blinked away tears. This trip was supposed to bring us together, but I was already letting him down.

Still facing the window, I asked, "What would you like to do for dinner?"

"How about a good steakhouse. Someplace nearby?"

"Sounds good."

Cesar finished dressing before me. "I'm going down to have a drink. I'll be in the lounge."

"Okay, I won't be long," I answered from the bathroom. Once I'd finished, I went looking for him. Except for the bartender, the lounge area was empty. I wandered the old hotel's maze of small rooms filled with antiques and finally located Cesar on the opposite side.

He stood beside a beautiful young woman. They'd bent their heads near one another as though engaged in a private conversation. The woman threw her head back, laughing at something he said. He chuckled, looking pleased, and their eyes met.

I stopped dead in my tracks, unable to look away. *We're here so Cesar can tell his mother about his sexual addiction, and he's flirting with another woman?* After taking a deep breath, I strode towards them.

Cesar smiled broadly and waved one arm towards me. "Kerry, I'd like you to meet Selena, the manager at this hotel. Selena, this is my wife."

I stood a bit taller and stuck out my hand. "Nice to meet you."

With a cool gaze, the woman grasped the ends of my fingers. Her faint smile never reached her eyes. "Hello," she said, "nice to meet you." She turned to resume speaking in Spanish to Cesar. Her face came alive and her eyes twinkled. She leaned close and giggled about something, touching his arm. I'd become an unwanted intruder.

Shaking with fury, I considered wrapping my arms about Cesar's waist to stake my claim but then thought better of the idea. *I'm not playing this game.* Instead, I slipped away to admire the furniture on display.

Cesar startled me by whispering in my ear. "Ready to go?"

"I've been waiting for you," I said.

"Do you know where you'd like to eat?"

"You wanted steak."

"It was just a suggestion," he said with a sudden disinterest.

Thrown off-balance by his shift in mood, I pulled out the phone and located a nearby restaurant. As we walked in silence, the tension mounted.

"Selena was just asking about our vacation rental business," Cesar finally said. "She's never been to Playa del Carmen."

"Oh?" I asked.

"She suggested we swap stays. We stay free at this hotel in exchange for her staying at one of ours," he said. "What do you think?"

"Why would a manager of a successful hotel in one of Mexico City's wealthiest areas be interested in staying at our condo? It makes no sense," I said. "Frankly, I think the idea came up because she has the hots for you."

"No... you're seeing things."

Was I? "She stood too close, touched you several times, and didn't even have the decency to be polite to me," I said. "I'm not seeing things. And frankly? You encouraged it." I squinted hard. "You were inappropriate, and I'm pissed you didn't include me more."

"I don't know what you're talking about." Cesar's mouth fell open.

"I don't buy that. You're not an idiot!" I said, though with less certainty. *Could I have gotten it wrong?*

The rest of the evening was quiet.

The next day we visited an outdoor marketplace. The open courtyard was lit with riotous colors. Rows of booths displayed traditional Mexican wares, from brightly decorated ceramics, beaded necklaces and bracelets, and embroidered dresses, to baskets and tapestries. Vendors manning small stalls vigorously waved.

At one of the nearest shops, Cesar lifted a cherry-red dress from where it'd hung on the wall. Across its bodice were embroidered orange, blue, and yellow flowers. "Gorgeous, what do you think of this?" he asked, holding it up.

With a glance, I said, "It's lovely but too small."

Cesar bent to speak to the hovering, small, wizened-faced older woman. "Do you have any extra-large dresses?" he whispered loud enough to be overheard.

I strolled down the aisle, pretending to admire her goods.

The vendor shook her head no but tugged his sleeve toward the men's shirts.

He patted her hand with a patient look. "They don't carry your size here, Gorgeous," he said in a boisterous voice.

I stole a glance at the bystanders as heat crept up my neck. "No problem," I murmured.

"What's wrong, Gorgeous?"

"It's embarrassing to look for clothing in a country that rarely carries my size. Can we focus on shopping for our rentals?"

"That's nothing to be uncomfortable about, Gorgeous. My mother always said I'm not the kind of guy who's attracted to Barbie dolls." He strutted towards me.

"That's a crappy thing to say!" I gasped.

"What?" Cesar's voice raised in shocked protest. "There's nothing wrong with not being a Barbie doll!"

"I can't believe you said that!" Tears welled. Cesar seemed to appreciate the hotel's manager's svelte figure.

"Well, it's true," he said smugly.

I squinted at him and considered the list of his weaknesses—his loss of a job, lack of money, the sexual impotence. *Don't do this,* my gut warned. *Cesar won't forget.* "You gotta know it's hurtful. What woman doesn't want to be seen as beautiful?"

"I don't know why that comment bothers you so much." He shrugged as he examined an item from off the shelf.

Was I being oversensitive? The men in my early life were often careless with other people's feelings. They were given a pass to be callous. We, women, catered to their every need, like hopping up to offer a fresh cup of coffee. Allowance was made when they lost their cool. It was just men being men.

The tension eased as Cesar and I wandered the stores and shared our finds. We poked fun at each other and laughed.

Later that night, we dressed to have dinner with Luisa, a woman I'd met on a language app. We'd become friends and agreed to meet if we were ever in the same area.

Cesar readjusted his belt buckle and checked his hair one more time. "You ready?"

"Yep," I answered and paused in the center of the room for his look of approval. Brad's eyes used to go bright, and he'd exclaim, "You look beautiful!" Cesar's gaze swept over me before he looked away. My smile faltered until I painted on a better one. Until now, it hadn't been a problem that Luisa's profile was of an attractive woman. As we walked to the restaurant, I wished the plans hadn't included Cesar.

Luisa was easy to spot in the empty dining room. I rushed to greet her with a big grin. "Luisa, this is Cesar," I said.

She nodded, only briefly meeting his eyes.

Over lasagna and red wine, we chatted in a mixture of both languages. Like a guard dog with its ears pressed back and raised hackles, I waited for Luisa and Cesar to strike up a conversation in Spanish. The earlier ease I enjoyed in the company of females was gone. Women had become dangerous competitors for Cesar's attention.

Throughout the meal, Luisa kept her focus on me. Her gaze never wavered from my face, nor did she ask Cesar a direct question.

As we stood to leave, she said to me, "Let me drop you off. It's on my way out of town."

"No, no, that's okay. It's no trouble to walk," I said.

"Please, I insist!"

Just as I'd feared, Cesar paused beside her passenger door as though considering riding beside her before he slid in next to me. Once the danger was past, I let go of the breath I'd been holding.

On the short ride, I watched Luisa navigate the narrow, busy streets. She'd shown me respect; maybe she'd even guessed I was in a troubled marriage. As a member of the Mexican culture, she could have acted as my interpreter, perhaps even become a confidant. Now that wasn't possible. In addition to the problem of distance, I no longer wanted Cesar around any woman.

For the past few months, I'd existed in a cocoon of shock, outrage, and grief. Earth-shattering betrayals had cut me off from the rest of the world. I no longer knew who could be trusted.

Luisa hopped out to hug me. "Stay in touch," she whispered.

I forced myself to let go and nodded.

Once behind the wheel, she lifted her hand to give a small wave and drove away. I lingered out on the empty side street to watch her taillights grow fainter until they winked out. It had started to mist; the raindrops mixed with my tears.

FAMILY

"You must remember, my dear lady, the most important rule of any successful illusion: First, the people must want to believe in it."
—Libba Bray, *The Sweet Far Thing*

Early December 2017

AFTER A FEW days exploring the capital, Cesar and I took a bus to see his mother. She lived a few hours away on the outskirts of a small town, the site of a former silver mine.

Outside the coach's window, the desert-brown landscape zipped past. Signs of Christmas were everywhere. Large red ornamental balls and golden stars adorned the tops of streetlights. Golden tinsel streamers decked doorways. A procession of people celebrating the Virgin of Guadalupe strode along a village roadside.

The slow back-and-forth rocking of the bus as it pulled to a stop woke me. Its brakes hissed. The driver swung a handle to open the front and back doors. Outside, a long line of families with children pushed forward.

"Back up, back up," the driver barked. "Let the people out."

Food vendors with pushcarts held up cans of soda and snacks. Against the depot's wall, a line of booths advertised tacos and tortas.

I stood curbside while Cesar grabbed our luggage. He took hold of my hand. "Let's hail a taxi and check into our hotel before we see my mom," he said.

We entered the massive bus depot, a dimly lit steel-framed building that echoed with a cacophony of noise. Cesar trotted across the large area, weaving among the milling people. He tugged at my hand, and I struggled to keep up. We exited into the noonday sunlight. My eyes stung in its brightness, and I raised my hand to block the glare.

Cars zipped past on a busy highway. Cesar neared the edge to hail a cab. An older dust-covered taxi crossed three lanes to stop beside us. Cesar leaned in through the vehicle's small window and spoke to the driver. He nodded curtly and hopped out to load our luggage.

Cesar opened the passenger door. "Go ahead, Gorgeous, get in."

The car's broad backseat leather was split with a thick wire spring peeking out of the opening. I gingerly crawled across, and Cesar scooted beside me, his leg pressed against mine.

The taxi shot off, dodging around the other cars. Cesar and I swayed, bumping into each other. Lightheaded with motion sickness, I hiccupped.

"Look." Cesar pointed towards one of the nearby hills.

I cranked my head and spied a distant statue of a man with his arms outstretched as if bestowing a blessing.

"That's the Cristo Rey, a marble cast of Christ. Would you like to take a drive to see it?"

"Let's see how things go with your mom," I said, suddenly spent.

"Okay." Disappointment crossed his face.

Since our arrival in Mexico, we'd worked nonstop, except for Cameron's visit. The stress of living in a foreign country left me exhausted. Cesar needed less sleep and stayed up late most nights to watch TV. The noise and light from the living room made it difficult for me to sleep.

The taxi let us off in front of a huge historic building, complete with a clocktower that faced the town square.

I gawked. "Wow, this is lovely."

We climbed the granite steps and entered the hotel. A wooden counter graced one side of the lobby, with a fireplace on the opposite wall. Stockings hung from an ornate mantle. A tall Christmas tree lit with twinkling lights and wrapped in a red ribbon stood at the back.

With a big grin, I looked around to take it in.

Once in the room, Cesar called his mother while I unpacked a few things. He hung up. "Mamita would love a visit once we get settled. I offered to take her out to dinner tonight. What do you think?"

"Sounds good."

I lay down while Cesar unpacked. "How do you feel about talking to your mom?" I rolled to face him.

"Okay." He met my eyes. "I'm going to wait until tomorrow to tell her. When we have some privacy."

"Makes sense," I said.

I'd only seen a few hazy photos of Cesar's dad. In one, the family posed in front of a cement wall. His parents were in the back, surrounded by their children. Cesar stood next to his dad, wearing a smile much too big for his face.

Whenever the topic of his father came up, Cesar's expression hardened. "Bad memories," he'd say, "I don't like to think about it."

One night while we lay in bed, Cesar told me a rare story about the man. His father was gone most days for business.

Cesar still lived at home as a young man. There'd been a family emergency. Unable to reach his father by phone, his mom had sent him to deliver the message. His dad was staying at a hotel several hours away. Cesar knocked on the door of the suite. A much younger woman answered.

"I fled to the lobby in a panic, then realized I didn't dare go home, or I'd get it from Mamita." Cesar blanched. "I didn't know what to do. Just then, Dad charged down, demanding to know why I was there." He broke off mid-sentence. I never learned what happened next.

Cesar returned to unpacking. I watched, wondering how he felt about telling his mom he'd become a cheater like his father.

I'd imagined the conversation countless times. The three of us would huddle close. As he broke the news, Mamita's eyes would fill with tears, and she'd clasp our two hands. Cesar would tell her, then me, that he was sorry, and we'd hug.

At dusk, we arrived at a single-story home in a small subdivision. Mamita leaned on a cane at the front gate. Her earlier knee surgery hadn't healed well. Cesar pulled her small frame into a big embrace. They both grinned ear to ear; then he re-introduced us.

The main room's walls were covered with colorful tapestries. A bookshelf lined with music CDs occupied the back corner. In the center sat a large rustic table.

"Please sit," Mamita said. She teetered before slumping into the nearest chair.

"*¿Mamita, quieres un vaso de agua?*" Cesar asked.

"*Por favor.*" She let out a slow breath as if in pain.

Cesar carried in three mismatched glasses of tepid water. I smiled thanks. The two of them chatted in Spanish. I caught enough to know they discussed our move and the new business.

Dogs barked outside, and the front door opened. Cesar's younger sister Marlena, a tall, willowy woman, entered, dropped her purse on the table, and slowly shrugged off her coat. A deep line creased her forehead right above her nose. Marlena swung her long hair free from the jacket before slinging the garment over the nearest chair.

She looked up. "Hello!" she said with a big smile. She kissed my cheek. "*Mucho gusto*, Kerry." Her eyes twinkled a warm brown.

"You too," I whispered back.

"Everyone hungry?" Cesar looked at the three of us. "Let's go eat."

On the short walk to the restaurant, Marlena and Cesar caught up, talking nonstop. Mamita looked tiny, sitting between her two children at the restaurant table. Marlena asked me something in Spanish a few times. I shrugged, lacking enough words to reply, and smiled.

Several hours later, we said our goodbyes with plans for the next day. To my surprise, the taxi dropped us off in front of a shopping mall.

"What are we doing here?" I asked.

"I need to pick up a few things," Cesar said.

"Some things?"

Cesar frowned. "Yeah, when I visit my family, it's expected I will buy Mamita a few supplies. It's my way of helping out."

"Do you mind if I sit and wait? My feet hurt." I pointed at an empty bench beside a cell phone vendor.

"I asked if you were up for this side trip on our way here."

I peered at him and tried to recall the conversation. "I didn't know you meant a shopping excursion," I muttered.

"Well, I have to do this." Cesar's voice rose. "I'll try to be quick about it." He strode towards the nearest women's clothing store.

An hour later, Cesar returned with two large store bags, one in each hand. "You ready?"

"Yeah." I pocketed my phone.

"C'mon, then." Oddly chastised, I followed him out.

On the taxi ride back to the hotel, I rested my head against his arm and dozed.

The next morning, we headed to the dining hall for breakfast. Tables set for four filled the empty cavernous room. A server seated us next to a floor-to-ceiling window that overlooked the city square. The sun shone through the frost that coated the glass.

I took a sip of orange juice.

"Today, I'm going to tell Mamita," he said. "Later on, my family wants to celebrate Christmas with us. Mamita asked us to pick up paella." He sipped his green juice.

"That sounds good."

"Great. It's settled, then." He took a bite of his food.

Mamita buzzed us through the front gate entrance and met us at the doorway with a big grin. We followed her slow limp back inside. Outside her bedroom door, there was the sound of a televised game show.

Cesar turned to me. "I'm going to talk to her now. We should be out in a bit." The two of them entered, shutting the door behind them.

I stood, shocked. Sounds of soft murmuring were audible. I'd expected—no, needed—to be a part of this conversation. *Should I knock and invite myself in?*

With a heavy sigh, I sat down at the kitchen table as tears streamed. This was supposed to be our moment. To bring us healing. To give me some closure. Cesar's mother had been so warm and accepting. She'd made me feel at home. She would understand what I'd been going through. Once again, I'd been left to deal with the pain alone.

An hour later, Cesar returned to the dining area, wearing a big smile. "That went well," he said. "Mamita was disappointed, of course, but we had a good discussion." Then he stared hard. "What's wrong, Gorgeous?"

"Nothing." I bent my head to hide the tears.

"What did I do wrong?" Cesar sounded irritated.

"I don't want to talk about it right now!" I hissed, pointing in his mother's direction. "Okay?"

With a stern look, he said, "Let's take a walk."

Like a child about to get scolded, I followed him outdoors.

Once out of earshot, Cesar asked, "Okay, now will you tell me what's going on?"

"I'd been looking forward to being a part of the conversation with your mom. She gets it, you know." I looked at him. "I've had nearly no one to talk to." My voice trailed off.

"Well, it's too late now," he grumbled. "I wished you had told me beforehand." He stared down the road with squinted eyes— his expression impenetrable. *Did he expect a congratulation for telling his mom, or was he angry that I'd wanted to be involved?* I fell silent. Protesting poor treatment had never served me well.

For the rest of the trip, I smiled and nodded at the appropriate times, a lifeless doll. We left for home a few days later.

My sons flew in to celebrate Christmas. From the outside, it would have appeared to have gone well. There was plenty of laughter as we lounged on sunny beaches, watched movies, and dined out. We taught Cesar the family's favorite card game and worked on a giant puzzle. Nothing was said about the marital struggles—my heart sank when it came time for my sons to leave.

With the holidays over, I put away the few Christmas decorations Cesar and I had bought. As I wrapped the last item in the tissue paper, an odd thought occurred. *How do I know if Cesar told his mother about the sexual addiction as he'd promised?*

Cesar lied about everything. He fibbed about inconsequential things, silly things, and essential things. He protected the truth like a starving dog with a bone. All I could be sure of was that he spoke to his mother. I had no way of knowing about what. I only had his word, and that was beginning not to count for much.

19

TRUTH & LIES

"A lie that is half-truth is the darkest of all lies."
—Alfred Tennyson

Mid-January 2018

IT WAS A snowy January afternoon when our plane landed in the sleepy Utah airport. Wind gusts whipped bursts of snow flurries into swirling white funnels, stinging my face. My thin jacket rippled and snapped, and I pulled my scarf tighter. *What will I learn tomorrow?* I shivered with fear. Cesar reached for my hand as we headed toward the car rental.

This was a quick trip—an overnighter. Tomorrow morning Cesar would take another polygraph test—his second. Since Maria's letter, I'd waffled about whether to stay. The answer depended on Cesar, but trying to decipher his investment was like reading tea leaves. One day he acted enthused, the next, numb. I wavered back and forth, unsure, scared of making the wrong decision.

Chuck had urged us to make this appointment, claiming it was a necessary part of Cesar's treatment. Between the high cost of the test and travel, I wasn't sure if we'd be back.

Cesar stood at the counter, hunched over the contract—confident, not nervous, as I would have expected. The clerk handed him a set of keys and pointed in the lot's direction. We stepped out into the blizzard-like conditions. I pinched my jacket's collar shut.

While Cesar loaded our carry-on luggage, I looked over my typed notes. For Cesar's last polygraph, I'd been caught unprepared. This time I'd come ready. My online coach helped with this new set of questions. These were designed to give a more accurate picture. My hands trembled as I moved the cursor down the list. Once I'd reached the end, I expelled a shaky breath.

Since Christmas, Cesar had become surly. Arguments would start over nothing. His lips would narrow into a thin line, and his face would darken. Leaping to his feet, he'd storm out of the house. Hours later, he'd return without giving an explanation.

He'd confessed that, during the break-up with his last wife, he choked her. "It was self-defense," he said. Recently, he reared up. "You're very lucky you're married to me now. When I was younger, I wasn't so nice." I'd heard the threat—more of a warning—there was a line I'd better not cross.

I suspected Cesar was back to watching porn. Most nights, he'd stay up late watching online videos. Though the streaming browser's history was filled with clips of people doing dumb things, there were gaps of missing time.

And he'd slipped again.

I'd discovered it while snooping. Instead of returning to bed after using the bathroom, I snuck Cesar's phone from its charging station. Except for the moonlight from the patio window, the living room was dark. *Don't do this,* I told myself. *It won't help.* The urge to know throbbed, monstrous and hungry. *It will only lead to more questions.* My hand operated as though guided by an outside force, and his home screen appeared. Among the messages to the family was a number I didn't recognize.

"Hey, beautiful! You have a sexy pout," Cesar had written in Spanish.

"What? Who is this?"

"An admirer!" He'd punctuated the sentence with a heart emoji.

"I don't know who you are."

"It's someone who would like to kiss your beautiful lips and hold that gorgeous body of yours," he texted.

"You have the wrong number." The conversation broke off.

My finger became thick and clumsy; I fumbled to snap several photos as proof before I doubled over in pain. The short text conversation replayed as I sat on the stool, shaking, icy cold. An overhead fan stirred the tiny bathroom's dank air.

Our sex life had dried up; days stretched into weeks. I had blamed the business. With the condos' construction nearing completion, most of our time was spent running from one appointment to the next. But Cesar hadn't lost interest in sex; he'd lost interest in me.

After he'd been diagnosed with sex addiction, I'd read everything I could find on the subject since it was never covered in graduate school. As an intimacy disorder, addicts prefer acting out fantasies with strangers and casual flings to being intimate with their long-term partners. There can't be any rejection if there isn't any love.

Once I understood trust and shame were root causes, I'd been working hard to show Cesar that he was safe. That I was on his side. *Why wasn't it working?*

Having no answers, I returned to the bedroom. As I reached for the charger, Cesar's snore broke off with a whistle, and he rolled to the edge, only inches away. I froze and held my breath; my lungs burned. He sputtered, then his chest rumbled with sleep. Shaking with relief, I finished plugging in his phone and jumped into bed, inhaling gulps of air.

At the sound of the alarm, neither of us moved. My midnight escapade had left my nerves jangling, and the pent-up words of what I'd found pressed for release. "Wanna tell me about those messages?"

Cesar peered at the ceiling, his face a mask. "It was a wrong number," he said dully, then added, "But I liked the sound of her voice." There it was, like a boxer finding his mark; Cesar had stuck me with a blow.

"Kerry, there's no need to sneak. If you want to see my phone, then just ask. Any time." I'd noticed he'd used my first name, another sign of rage. He'd pull it out like a weapon, so I'd know I'd fallen out of favor. He turned to look at me; his voice was soft. "Okay?"

I studied him for a long moment, confused by his sudden mood change and the odd message. *Just ask? Could I demand he turn over his phone? Walk up, hold out my hand, and tell him I want to see it?* I stifled a snort. *And would he actually do it?* I wasn't so sure I believed him. Something was off—maybe a hidden advantage I couldn't see. "Yeah, I hear you." Still hurt by his early comment about the woman's voice, I gave him a cool stare. "Shouldn't we get going?" I said before turning away to hide my face.

The slam of the rental car door brought me back. Cesar slid behind the wheel. "Where are we staying again?"

We arrived at the hotel at dusk. In the strangely silent room, I unpacked a few toiletries and washed my face for bed. Cesar ironed his slacks, his face inscrutable.

He clicked off his phone. "Ready for lights out?"

"Mmm-hmm," I murmured.

In the darkness, he scooted close until our bodies pressed like spoons. He kissed my head and then relaxed into sleep. The familiarity of his gesture eased a few of my fears.

The next morning there was a hushed solemnity. We readied like two people dressing for a funeral. I stopped brushing my teeth to stare at the mirror. My image was ghostlike. The green and yellow flecks in my irises glowed against the paleness of my skin.

"You coming?" Cesar called out.

"Yeah, just a second." And I snatched my jacket.

Chuck had moved since our last visit. His office was a short drive away. Instead of a lobby, the front entrance was a tiny stoop that faced a staircase. I looked around, lost.

Chuck leaned over the top railing. "There's seating up here," he called out. "I'll be with you in a minute."

We waited in opposite seats on the landing. I fiddled with my purse strap while Cesar busied himself, swiping something off his phone.

Finally, Chuck reappeared. "Okay, you two." He gestured us down the hallway into a replica of his old office with the same desk and Japanese swords.

"It seems to have been a hard few months." Chuck looked first at Cesar and then at me. Neither of us spoke.

"It's good to schedule these every three months until you've secured sobriety." He paused, his eyes darting between the two of us. The tension mounted. I twisted my knuckles and fought the urge to crack them. "Do either of you have concerns you'd like to bring up before Cesar takes the test?"

"Yeah, I do." I looked up. "I have two." My heart beat faster.

"Okay?"

"Can polygraphs be fooled?" I asked. "Several online videos claim they can."

"That's tough to do unless the examinee is a sociopath." Chuck gave a feeble smile. "We, of course, ruled that diagnosis out Cesar's first go-around."

I raised an eyebrow. "You sure?" Fearing I'd said too much, I looked away.

"Yeah, I'm sure the results will be accurate."

"Okay," I said, unconvinced. The second question stuck in my craw. I forced myself to spit out, "Is it necessary to review the questions before the polygraph?" I paused. "I'd prefer we didn't." Sweat dripped down my neck.

Chuck gave a slight smile. "It'd be easier that way, but no, we need to go through them first." His eyes met mine. "Are you afraid if Cesar hears them, he'll have time to prepare?"

No, I'm afraid of what he might do to me, I thought, but nodded to drop the subject.

"No, it doesn't give him an edge." He glanced at both of us. "Any more questions?"

"No," Cesar said. I shivered at the menacing sound of his voice.

"I'm good too," I lied.

"Okay, let's go over your list." Chuck picked up a pen and notepad.

In my shaking hand, the words ran together. "First, 'Is there anything about your sexual history that you haven't told your wife?'" The rushing roar of my blood drowned out my voice.

"Second question: 'Were you purposely deceptive during the first disclosure process?'"

I pried my dry tongue from the roof of my mouth. "Three: 'Have you purposely omitted any sexual behaviors from your last disclosure?'"

The phone slipped. I wiped off my sweaty palms and picked it up. The office was deathly quiet.

"Four: 'Have you had physical, sexual contact, including oral sex, with any person other than what you have disclosed?'" My online coach had insisted I ask this one. "You never know, Kerry. Assume nothing," she'd said.

"Five: 'Have you intentionally viewed any pornography since the last disclosure?'" There wasn't any doubt in my mind about the answer to this one.

"Six: 'Have you patronized any sex-oriented businesses since the last disclosure?'" These words echoed in the still room.

At the last question, I hesitated, trembling with fear, and then took a big inhale. "And finally, seven: 'Did you marry me primarily for financial gain?'" Wrung out, I flopped back. With burning cheeks, I studied an imaginary dot. My breath thundered in the eerie silence.

Finally, Chuck spoke. "Okay, those are good. But I think we could capture their intention a little differently." He bent over his notebook and scribbled. "What do you think of these?"

A loud hum buzzed in my ears. Except for the last question, the new ones were anemic versions of the originals. *No, no, no!* I stared, dumbstruck, and weighed the cost of putting up a fight. Chuck had shared when we first met that he was a recovered sex addict. *Was he trying to sabotage the process?*

Chuck glanced up. "What do you think?"

Spent, I nodded in defeat. "Yeah, they're fine," I said in a dead voice. I snuck a peek at Cesar. He stared transfixed, his face a rigid mask.

I sent Chuck several desperate looks.

Ignoring me, he said, "Okay, let's have the two of you go to the waiting area while I meet with the examiner."

What?? You're leaving me with Cesar? Dark spots swam across my vision. I wobbled and blinked away tears as I trailed behind the men. Once seated on the landing, I braced for what might come next, my nerves stretched thin, and traced the carpet's black pattern with my eyes. Up, left, down, over to the right. The clock on the far wall ticked. Cesar's fury pulsed.

A rustling came from his direction; my muscles froze like a rusted metal joint. *What's the worst he can do?* I whispered and stole a glance.

With a deadpan face, Cesar removed one card after another from his wallet. "Here, I won't be needing these," he said. I gaped at the fistful of credit cards he'd handed to me. He stiffened upright to stare straight ahead.

Chuck re-entered. "Cesar, the examiner's ready." Tight-lipped, Cesar rose to his feet and walked like a man on death row out of the room.

I bolted for the rental car, sobbing. *We're over because I dare question why he married me?* A second thought occurred. *I could be done with this and leave. And, to do what? Return to the empty life I'd had before?* I shuddered a no.

Instead, I dialed my mother. Shortly after Christmas, I had filled her in with as few words as possible.

"Kerry, I was just thinking about you—" My mother said, her voice cheerful.

"He's leaving me, Mom!"

"What?"

"We're in Utah for a counseling session, and he's furious." My voice broke; I hiccupped between sobs. "I think we're over." I burst into another round of tears.

"Oh, honey. I'm so sorry."

"Please pray. I need to go but pray! Okay?" I rooted around my purse for a tissue.

"Okay, honey," she said. Her voice was soft with concern.

I hurried inside.

At the sound of the front door closing, Chuck called out, "We're up here. The polygraph is finished." I re-entered the office to find both men waiting. Cesar sat stone-faced.

"I have the results," Chuck said. "Cesar, you've passed."

I exhaled loudly and turned to Cesar with a big smile, figuring he'd be pleased too. The nightmare was over, and things could return to normal.

He sat still, his expression cold.

Time slowed to a crawl. Chuck's mouth moved, but his voice sounded distant over the ringing in my ears. Cesar nodded to something Chuck said, and the two men stood.

Chuck shook both of our hands. "Well, you know how to get a hold of me should you need anything?" And with that, he held the door.

I staggered out to the parking lot. On the drive to the airport, I sat riveted to my seat. Cesar clenched the steering wheel.

After several miles passed, he broke the silence. "It's hit me that what I'm experiencing right now has been how you've been feeling since I betrayed you." He glanced at me. "Right?" he asked.

I inhaled sharply. After months of being cut off and alone, I'd ached to hear these words. Finally, someone, and not just anyone, understood.

"Yes! That's exactly how I've been feeling," I gasped. With that, I burst into tears again—this time with relief.

20

CHASING INTIMACY

"No one can make you feel inferior without your consent."
–Eleanor Roosevelt

Spring, 2018

WITH THE TRIP to Utah out of the way, we jumped back into managing our fledgling business. The two new condos were nearing completion.

We'd arrived at the job site for a meeting with a team of real estate agents to find the newly installed elevator was out of order. I paused on the second landing of the five-story building, heaving, out of breath.

"You doing okay, Gorgeous?" Cesar peered over the railing; his voice echoed down the shaft.

"Yeah..." Staring at the next set of steps, I wiped the sweat from my brow—*three more flights to go*–and tugged the shirt free of my sticky back. The dank air grew hotter as we climbed. It was another scorching spring day in Playa del Carmen.

At the fifth-floor landing, I bent over, panting. My left knee throbbed in time to the pounding of my heart.

"The meeting starts in a few minutes." Cesar tapped his thigh impatiently outside the condo door.

"I know." I fumbled for the keys.

Once inside, Cesar went in one direction and I in the other. He called out from the guest bathroom, "They haven't installed the sink yet. Not the plugs either."

"Uh-huh," I said as I opened the new master bedroom's curtains to stare out at the city view. A brightly colored mural of a woman's face painted on a nearby building looked back at me. A pair of young boys raced across the flat rooftops while their mother hung laundry on a clothesline.

There was a rap on the front door.

"Gorgeous, the real estate people are here," Cesar said.

"Okay," I sighed. My stomach flipped over. For the past few months, I'd struggled with bouts of severe diarrhea that came and went. *It's the stress. Once this project is done, life will get better,* I told myself. I pasted on a friendly smile to greet the two agents.

Since arriving home from Utah, Cesar and I had settled into an uneasy truce. *Cesar's too scared to trust,* I thought. *He just needs time to discover he's safe with me.* During the twenty years I'd counseled, a few trauma clients spent a year or more in treatment before they'd grown comfortable enough to discuss sensitive matters. *Maybe that's the case for Cesar.*

"Did you ever play a children's game at school when you dance in a circle with your classmates?" I asked him one morning while we lay in bed.

"A children's game?"

"It's more of a song," I said. "Well, maybe a game. It's something we played at school." In a wavering voice, I sang the lyrics of swinging different parts of the body into the inner circle of kids. First, it was the hand, the foot, the leg, and so on. "Ever play that game?"

"I don't think so..." he said.

"Well, you eventually hop in and out of the circle as you sing," I said. "Our marriage sometimes feels like we're playing the game, only when it comes to putting all of yourself into the circle, you don't."

He studied me for a long second. "I don't know what you want from me." He puffed loudly. "Can we talk about something else?"

I stared, perplexed. *What will it take to break through that armor of fear?* I wondered. *What if I can't?* I pushed that thought away.

Shortly after Christmas, Cesar had started to see Augusto, a male psychologist, for therapy. Sometimes he came home from their twice-a-week sessions talkative. Other times he appeared sullen, often waiting days before he'd share some tidbit he'd discovered about himself, his addiction, or his childhood. My optimism about us waxed and waned. Cesar would do something that sent me spinning with excitement, only to dash it with a terse look, critical remark, or disinterest in sex.

One weekend morning, we hung out at a beach club. The server set two margaritas on the table beside us.

"Cheers," Cesar said.

"Cheers." Our glasses clinked. After taking a sip, I'd leaned back to relax under the shade of a palapa.

"Augusto thinks I need to do something that's all my own. Maybe a job."

I sat upright. "What?" Though the condo construction was finishing, there was still much to do. Then there was the running of the business.

"And I agree with him." Cesar looked away.

I blinked furiously, shocked by this news. *How could he be considering this just as the company is opening?* Panic surged at the thought of all the tasks that would fall to me. There would be guest check-ins, maintenance issues, getting supplies, and scheduling cleaning crews— all in a foreign language. Tears burned against the back of my eyelids.

"I've been thinking about getting into real estate," Cesar said.

Real estate? I swallowed hard. Several developers had thrown opening parties. In the dimly lit construction sites, new buyers were served copious amounts of liquor while loud music blared. Scantily dressed agents gave tours. The entire scene reminded me more of a dance club than a business setting. Then, the job would comprise of communicating at odd hours, primarily by text, with potential clients—some of whom would be women.

"I've met someone who manages a small realty. He said he could really use the help—just for the summer." Cesar glanced over. "But that's only if you're okay with this."

How could Augusto have encouraged this? A sex addict selling real estate? That's about as wise as an alcoholic tending bar. I stared out at the water as I searched for the right words. *No, I'm not okay with this.* "I don't know..." My voice trailed off. This was a lose-lose proposition. If I said yes, then I couldn't complain about his long work hours and dealings with strangers, but I'd be the distrusting bitch if I said no.

"Think about it." The subject came back up a few days later. Seeing no way out, I agreed to meet with the real estate manager.

We arrived at a local yogurt shop mid-day. The outdoor cafe patio was covered by a large awning and sat at a busy street intersection. Only a few other customers occupied the nearby tables.

A few minutes after the hour, a lanky man strolled towards us. "Hi, I'm Elias," he said with a toothy grin. His outstretched hand enveloped mine; his firm grasp pinched. "Please, please sit," he said with a wave.

A teenage server interrupted the introductions to take our drink orders in Spanish.

"I'm excited to have you join our small firm," Elias told Cesar. "Currently, we have three agents, all new to the business." He listed the job's responsibilities.

I listened, confused. This didn't sound like a summer position. I considered interrupting but dismissed it as a bad idea. Wives weren't to make a public display of putting husbands on the spot; we were to know our place. Instead, I nodded to show interest.

"Okay, then. It's settled." Elias stood to his feet. "I'll see you at the office tomorrow at 9:00 a.m." With a big smile, he patted Cesar's shoulder.

Cesar rose. "Sounds good!" he told Elias.

I followed Cesar back to the car.

"What was that all about?" I asked.

"What?" Cesar sounded surprised.

"You said this was for the summer, but he just hired you for a permanent position."

"I don't know what you're talking about," Cesar said. "Why would Elias offer something temporary?"

"I have no idea why, but that's what you said."

"I'm sorry you got the wrong impression." Cesar thumped the steering wheel with his thumb and blew out a loud breath.

I looked out the side window. The air between us thickened. *Why was he so mad?* Lunch rolled over in my stomach. I clutched at my belly and burped. "So, what do you think of Elias?" I asked, trying to move the discussion onto safer ground. "First impressions?"

Cesar parked in the underground garage before he spoke. "Elias is young and tries hard, but he's too nice with the other guys in the office," he said. "I think I can help him."

"Well, that will be good for both of you," I said. "Hey, would you like to go for a swim?" I hoped this offer would decrease the tension.

"Sure." Cesar helped me out of the vehicle.

Once in the pool, I stood with my back against the jet of warm water, trying to ease my tense shoulders. Cesar jumped in behind me. Laughing, I swam over and planted a kiss. "I know you need something that's all your own. I get it," I said. "I was just surprised by the job and thought you said was it temporary, but that's okay." I beamed. "Elias seems like a great guy."

Cesar sat me down and, without another word, got out.

I threw my hands up. "What did I say now?"

Stony-faced, he took a seat on one of the lounge chairs. Blinking away tears, I swam several more laps. The sun had set, and the evening air had cooled by the time I stepped out of the pool. We spent the rest of the night in tense silence.

I awoke to the blaring noise of Cesar's phone alarm and squinted at the hour. It was early. He hopped out of bed and pulled on exercise clothes. "I'm going for a jog and then grabbing some green juice before heading into the office." With a quick kiss, he left.

I buried my head in the pillows and tried to fall back to sleep. The new business would open soon; my chest tightened at this thought, and I rushed to the bathroom, sick. In the mirror reflection, dark circles lined my eyes. *We need to get away. Do something different*, I thought. Back in bed, I searched online for someplace exotic for a weekend stay.

Cesar came home at lunch, excited about his morning at the office, the earlier foul mood gone.

"Guess what?" I said.

"What?"

"I booked us a weekend at Xpu-Ha beach. *Glamping*."

"Glamping?"

"It's a cross between camping and staying at a nice hotel," I said.

Cesar's eyebrows rose.

"On beds, not on the floor," I laughed.

That weekend, it rained. We spent most of the two days inside a sizable watertight canvas tent instead of lounging on the beach. It was set atop a varnished deck and had a full-sized bathroom.

The place was beautiful—romantic. Large tapestries adorned the interior walls, and a soft area rug covered the floor. A red comforter with matching pillows lined with golden tassels decorated the king-sized bed. In the flickering candlelight, I kissed Cesar's chest before straddling him. He held my hips as I took him. His dark eyes never left my face. "I love you," I whispered and arched my back with an orgasm.

He collapsed next to me, panting. "Love you more," he said; his voice was hushed. I snuggled close and was wrapped in his arms. We awoke from a brief nap, hungry, and ordered room service. For those two days, we re-acquainted ourselves with one another. A sweetness reminiscent of our time dating briefly returned. Later, I'd come to see that time had been a quiet respite as an upcoming storm gathered strength.

With the weekend over, we returned to our new schedule of Cesar spending mornings at the realty office. Early that week, I awoke sick with a wracking cough. Cesar heard me vomit.

"You need to see a doctor." He laid his hand on my forehead. "You're burning up."

Within minutes of entering the ER, I was admitted. The nurse hung an IV bag of antibiotics. She paused awkwardly for a moment. "You're really ill. Do you know that?"

Another spasm of coughing bent me over. "Yeah, yeah, I know." I waved my hand in the air. "I'm prone to bronchitis."

"No, no, that's not it. It's your white blood count. It's sky-high, but we can't find the infection."

"I don't have pneumonia?" I looked up in surprise.

"No, your x-ray was clear, but your bloodwork showed something very serious is wrong." She shook her head, puzzled. "Have you ingested anything? Drank the water, maybe?"

That night, in the semi-darkened room, Cesar pulled a chair close. With hooded eyes, he reached for my hand. "Seeing you like this makes me realize how much I'd miss you." With his head drooping, he appeared close to tears. I nodded slowly. *You'd miss me?* I thought, puzzled.

The next day, the hospital discharged me with a regimen of new medications. Soon, our kitchen counter was lined with several different-colored boxes and bottles of drugs. For days, the mildest of efforts made me pant. I'd have to stop to rest until my rapid heart rate slowed. I'd never felt more feeble. More mortal.

This illness drove home my isolation. With the online coaching group wrapped up, I'd found myself alone. Cesar and I had started attending a local church, but I hadn't gotten close to any women. I decided to check out a Bible study one of them had started in her home.

It'd been a while since I'd gotten therapy, but I needed the help. A social media post advertised English-speaking counseling; I made an appointment with a social worker.

Suzanne rang me into her second-floor apartment that doubled as a counseling practice. Dressed in flowing linen pants and shirt, the slender woman walked as though gliding. We passed through her modest kitchen and living room, sparsely decorated with bare counters, and entered an office. She sat behind a wooden desk and brushed a few strands of blonde hair from her eyes.

"How can I be of help?" she asked with a thick accent.

In a few words, I described my move to Mexico and marital difficulties.

She nodded. "That's a lot to go through."

My mind flashed to last night's argument.

We'd sat at a car repair center, waiting for service.

Out of the blue, Cesar announced, "I've decided to practice sobriety."

"Okay..." I tensed for what would come next.

"Yeah, I'm committing only to think sexually about my wife, no other woman."

My eyes bulged. "What??"

"Don't start judging me!" he growled.

"I'm just trying to understand!"

"There you go getting all critical!" He exited the car, slamming the door behind him.

I looked around the parking lot, speechless. It hurt to learn he'd been fantasizing about others and that he'd leave instead of working it out.

He returned home hours later. "I needed to cool off, so I went out for a few drinks," he said to no one in particular.

Suzanne's voice pulled me from the memory. "I think I can help. Imagine you're sitting next to an empty chair and Cesar's across the room. You've invited him to join you, but it's up to him to walk over." Her warm eyes were kind, but her voice was matter-of-fact. "You can't make him do it. You're trying to, though. And working hard at it, but it's up to him. He has to do the work."

I clutched at my purse and shook my head. *No... that's not going to work.* I stared hard at her while trying to think of how to explain that this situation was different. My fragile connection to Cesar was weakening. Soon, it'd finish breaking.

Suzanne looked at me quizzically and waited.

Every argument I considered was familiar. And, as a practiced psychologist, I already knew the answer. For a long moment, no one spoke.

"So, what am I supposed to do?" I cringed at the sound of my whiny voice. Tears threatened to fall. "Nothing?"

"I know it feels like doing nothing, but you can't make someone cross the room to be with you. He has to do that on his own." She looked at her notes; a crease appeared above her forehead. She opened her mouth and hesitated for a split second. "Kerry, by the time you've realized one of your boundaries has been crossed, it's already occurred way back there." With that, she extended her entire arm to point out at the street.

My mouth fell open. Was she going to become another Chuck and push me to leave? My mind fogged as I struggled to grasp what she was telling me. It sounded important, but its significance eluded me.

21

ONE SMALL STEP

"When your lover is a liar, you and he have a lot in common, you're both lying to you!"
—Susan Forward, *When Your Lover Is a Liar: Healing the Wounds of Deception and Betrayal*

Mid-July 2018

THE JET SHUDDERED; several nearby tray tables clunked. My stomach suddenly dropped, making my head woozy. I looked out the passenger window.

Today was Cesar's birthday. All the ingredients to make his favorite cake sat out on the kitchen counter, but instead of celebrating with him, I was on a plane headed for Phoenix. Several clouds, resembling hand-spun cotton candy, floated past my jet window unnoticed. Despite my best efforts, our marriage was unraveling.

Things had been deteriorating for a while. In addition to the serious relapses was a more subtle disintegration. It was as if we were coming apart in slow motion. Cesar stayed up later, did more things alone, such as jogging and running errands, and then got a job. All seemingly good things, but I suspected ulterior motives. More freedom meant Cesar could get into more trouble while I remained none the wiser.

Conversations went awry and spun off in weird directions. An innocuous question, like "How are you doing?" had become a direct challenge. Most days, we vacillated between silent retreats and passive-aggressive attacks. Our *Love You More* game had been relegated to being played when Cesar was half asleep or drunk, a cruel reminder of what was missing. Just as he'd complained in his letter to Maria, our marriage had become a prison, and I, his jailer. Cesar had decided it was time to take a break. Rather than waiting for him to leave first, I'd boarded for Phoenix with a one-way ticket.

The plane jostled, and the items in the front cabin shook noisily. After re-reading the same paragraph several times, I shut off my phone.

Mamita's knee had taken a turn for the worse. The kneecap was swollen and mottled-angry red. Mamita seldom left her bed. Cesar and his siblings had decided she should stay with us. Some of the best orthopedic surgeons in Mexico had nearby offices, and our home was wheelchair-ready.

Cesar often wished for closer family relationships. Each morning, he'd read through their private group chat, filled with inspirational quotes and funny memes. He'd slip on his glasses to read me a few of his favorites. Sometimes, he pulled the wire frames off to rub his eyes.

"Look," he said. "I've deleted all of the pictures. Read it." He shoved the phone in my direction. "See? All it says is, 'Good morning' over and over and the same thing with 'Good night.'" He ran his finger down the page. "That's all we say to each other—good morning and good night. That's not a real conversation."

"So be the first to start," I'd replied. "Set an example."

"I'm not sure that's a good idea." He sighed. "Someone probably will weigh in like they do about my soda pop habit. You know the crap I take for that."

"Then ignore it. You don't have to participate," I said. "Especially if you think it's a waste of time."

"Oh no! I don't dare do that either." He gave a snort. "Trust me, I've tried. I'll hear all about it at the next family gathering."

On our first date, Cesar had shared how he'd been the family's scapegoat. His older siblings had gotten approval for working hard at school or on the job, and the younger two had been favored as the babies. He and his middle sister went largely ignored. "We always stuck together. We had to," he said.

Early on, Cesar discovered he had the gift of charm. With money tight, he did odd jobs to earn some extra spending cash.

"I'd dress up in my Sunday best and carry newspapers rolled under my arm. I kept them inside a flattened cardboard box, folded in half like an envelope flap to keep the black ink from staining my clothes." He demonstrated. "I would sell them to people commuting home." I'd picture him as a young boy walking the busy sidewalks, hocking papers.

"And I'd shoeshine too." He drew his lips together like he was about to blow a whistle and make a squeaking noise as he rapidly swung his hands back and forth in a buffing motion. He glowered. "I had to give some of what I earned to my little brother, or Mamita threatened to tell Dad," he said. "According to Dad, no kid of his was gonna be out hustling for work." He scowled. "When Mamita dies, I'm not going to her funeral."

"Cesar, you don't mean that. Of course, you'll go," I said.

"What does it matter; she'll be gone anyways." He shrugged.

In the public eye, Cesar acted the part of a doting son, yet in private, he brooded about how no one had stood up for him, loved him better, or had kept him safer.

"What about including her in some of your therapy with Augusto," I said.

His eyebrow drew together. "Hmm... I hadn't thought of that," he muttered. "Maybe... if Mamita is interested." He added, "And, if she's feeling up for it, of course."

We met Mamita at the airport several days later. She'd arrived in a wheelchair, barely able to walk. During the first week, she met with a doctor for an assessment and x-rays. Two surgeries were scheduled: one right away and a second a few months later. Most days she rested with her leg elevated, too ill to do more.

Cesar and I kept busy taking his mother to appointments and checking in the guests of our newly opened business. After one particularly long morning, we stopped to pick up a few groceries.

"Stay in the air conditioning. There's no need for both of us to go in," Cesar said.

"Okay, thanks," I sat back to rest in the quiet when an outbound call came through the car's speakers. Maria's phone number flashed across the radio display. Just as it suddenly appeared, it disappeared.

He's done it again. Icy cold adrenaline froze my limbs, and my mind went blank.

The sound of Cesar popping the trunk to load the grocery brought me out of a foggy numbness. "I think I got everything," he said in a too bright voice with too big of a grin.

"Who did you call?" I asked softly.

He looked away to buckle his seatbelt. "Elias. I had a few questions about a piece of real estate," he said with a deadpan face.

"Elias has an out-of-state phone number?" I asked. "That's odd, especially considering the area code was Maria's."

There was a long pause.

"You're right. It was Maria. I just didn't want to upset you," he said. "I found her number when I cleaned out my briefcase." He paused. "Her dad was a physician. Did you know that? I wanted her opinion about Mamita."

"No, I didn't know..." *A likely story.* "Don't you think you should have talked to me before calling her?"

"Yeah, you're right." He blew a long breath. "I should have."

A deep weariness replaced the fading adrenaline buzz. The cityscape whizzed by my window, but I felt too tired, beat up, and worn out to notice. *At what point is a marriage over?* I again wondered. *Cesar says he's never worked harder to get better. Was it cold-hearted to walk out on someone who's trying?*

How does a marriage end? Do two people one day wake up and know it's over? Was our relationship troubled or terminal? Maybe if I had hard evidence that Cesar's commitment was gone, I would feel free to leave.

There were plenty of signs, but Cesar always had a good excuse. Several sexual-performance-enhancing pills had gone missing. At least I thought so, but I couldn't remember how many we'd bought or the number of times we'd been intimate. Most evenings, Cesar went around the corner block for a *paleta*, a flavored popsicle. He'd leave his phone sitting on the table. Had he forgotten it, like he said, or was he evading the location-sharing app? And I snooped again, this time through his computer, and found he'd visited page after page of sex workers' advertisements. When confronted, he claimed their clips were better than porn.

Were these incidents enough? I struggled to let go for fear of getting it wrong. There would be no takebacks.

It was still early evening when we sat down to watch TV. "Hey, let's go to bed early." My smile hinted at more.

Cesar didn't look up.

I snuggled closer. "What do you think?"

He bristled, his body stiffening. "You know, I'm way more sensitive about how you're doing. I'm careful not to bring up sex if I think you're not well."

"Oh..." My face flushed hot. "Okay." I moved to another chair and busied myself with some emails.

As the TV show's credits rolled across the screen, Cesar glanced in my direction. "Yeah, let's go to bed early; it's a good idea."

"Sure!" I smiled, pleasantly surprised.

He stopped at the bedroom doorway. "Hey, let me say goodnight to Mamita first."

"Okay." I got around and waited in bed.

Five, then fifteen minutes passed. Soon, it was half an hour. Hurt anger replaced my earlier excitement. *What's taking so long?* I wondered.

An hour later, Cesar carried in a tall glass of iced mineral water. His eyes glowed. "I had a great talk with Mamita." He reached out to hand me the drink. "Here, I got you something, too."

I stared at the water, confused, not sure to be thankful or enraged. "You said you were going to say goodnight. It's been over an hour, and we have to get up early for an appointment." My face tightened with anger.

"I can't believe this. It's never enough with you." He slammed drawers as he undressed. "I'll have you know I'm not going to be rude to my mom." Once in bed, he peered over at me. "Ready for lights out, Gorgeous?" His voice was oddly calm.

After taking a sip, I sat the glass on the nightstand. It had been weeks since we'd last been intimate—one of the rare ways we connected. I'd made the mistake of getting my hopes up. "I've been ready for an hour." Tears leaked.

Once the lights were out, Cesar parted my legs to rub the top of my clitoris. I grimaced.

"Lower, a little lower," I whispered.

He continued as though he hadn't heard. What began as a pleasant sensation burned as though on fire. Frantic, I pushed his hand and scrambled to get away.

He flipped me, mid-air, upside-down; his finger never left the spot. A blinding orgasm exploded, and I moaned.

"What was that?" I leaped away from him.

"What?" His voice rose in innocent protest.

"That! It hurt, that's what!" I charged out of the room as tears spilled.

"I don't know what your problem is," he called out.

Cesar was sleeping when I returned. I watched him while I considered my options. Not wanting Mamita to know we were having problems, I crawled back into bed. My crotch throbbed. *This can't continue,* I thought. *But if I up and leave, I risk the business and most of my money. Am I prepared to start over broke? And where? Mexico? Or the United States?* Hours later, I fell into a fitful sleep.

Things weren't going well with Suzanne, my therapist. Just as I'd feared, an unspoken pressure to leave Cesar hung over every session. Not having the energy to fight another front, I fired her and found Lisa, a social worker with a trauma specialty.

Each week, Lisa started the session by adjusting her simple sundress' hem. She'd swing her long blonde hair off her shoulder.

"Kerry, when you feel paralyzed around Cesar, is it an old emotion or a new one?" She crossed her legs and waited.

I cocked an eyebrow.

"Do you know what I mean?" A crease appeared above her nose.

"Have I had the feeling before? Like when I was a kid?"

"Exactly."

"Hmm..." I bit my lower lip. "Sometimes I'm afraid when I'm around Cesar. Worried. You know, like he's going to reject me," I said slowly. "That's an old feeling." I nodded to myself. "Yeah, very old." We locked eyes.

"You've been a good mom. Try using that part to comfort the fear."

"Okay...?"

"Whenever you're having a strong reaction or struggling to stand up for yourself, I want you to ask, 'Is this an old feeling or a new one?'"

I nodded hesitantly.

"And if it's old, give yourself a mental hug. Be the mother you need," she said. "Okay?" Her eyes softened.

"Okay," I said softly. "I'll try."

With Cesar's birthday fast approaching, I suggested we celebrate with a weekend in Cozumel.

"You know I don't like the fuss," he said.

"That doesn't mean we can't start something new."

He frowned. Later, in bed, he said, "I need to get away. To think things through."

I bolted upright. "What?"

"I've been giving this a lot of thought. I need to take a few days," he said. "As kind of a retreat to think through our marriage."

My heart pounded. "Think through what?"

"Whether our marriage is working,"

"You're going to take a few days away to decide if you want to stay in this relationship?"

"Is that a problem for you?" he sputtered.

I choked up. "What am I supposed to do? Wait, alone, and carry on while you try to make up your mind?" I said between sobs.

"...is that not allowed?" His voice dripped with sarcasm.

"Of course, it's allowed." I rolled to my side. "Good night."

"Good night."

He expects me to sit home and wait like a good little girl while he decides if he wants to stay married? My blood pulsed. *What if he decides we're over? Old or new feelings?* I asked myself. *Old... very old.*

I slipped into the darkened living room. In the city lights, misshapen shadows danced on the tile floor. I typed a short text to an old high school friend. "Things are bad. Can I come to stay for a few days?"

A few minutes later, she replied, "Of course. Whatever you need."

"Okay, I'll see you tomorrow," I answered.

My hand shook as I packed a few things early the next morning. Cesar stirred. "What are you doing?"

"I'm visiting a friend in the States. An old girlfriend of mine."

"Oh?" He blinked to clear the sleep from his eyes.

"And I need to leave in fifteen minutes. Can you give me a ride?"

Wide-eyed, he threw on some shorts. We rode the hour-long drive to the airport in silence.

Below the jet, the Arizona desert browns drifted past. *What's wrong with me?* A lump formed in my throat. *I'm afraid... of his ridicule and upsetting him. I want us to work. To be happily married. To be a couple. I want to be loved. Why doesn't he love me?*

Tamara stood waiting outside the security gate. After a quick hug, she drew back. "You can stay as long as you want. You're family, okay?"

And with that said, we left.

22

GOING CRAZY

"Facts do not cease to exist because they are ignored."
—Aldous Huxley, *Complete Essays 2, 1926-29*

Mid-July–Late August 2018

I CHECKED MY online Mexican bank account again. *Was this the fifth or sixth time?* I wondered as I paced Tamara's home like a caged tiger. It'd never occurred to me Cesar might raid it. Earlier today, he'd made a large cash withdrawal and then sent photos of a trip he had made to Cozumel.

"I thought we'd tour that place together?" I messaged back.

"You left. I decided to do something special for my birthday."

"Send me a selfie."

"Why?"

"Because I don't believe you're there by yourself." *Like he would take one of him and a girlfriend?* I shook my head and scrambled to think of a better way to prove he wasn't alone. Cesar shut off his phone.

I was being punished for leaving. Of course, he'd deny that. But his tactic had worked; it hurt.

Tamara's home was a quiet respite, despite the comings and goings of her large family. I'd been so immersed in the experience of living with Cesar—born out of necessity—that I hadn't realized he'd been taking over my life. At first, he offered helpful advice, but, over time, it'd become criticism. He'd started to ask, "What are you doing?" whenever I concentrated on a project. Without conscious awareness, though, I limited my activities to avoid unwanted suspicion.

The break from Cesar's intense scrutiny was a relief. I used the freedom to comb through several of his phone backups. Despite his numerous reassurances that I had the right to check his browser history and text messages, I hadn't felt free to do so. There was what he said, and then there was how he behaved. His actions disagreed. I was smart enough to know any such request wouldn't be welcomed.

What I found was horrifying. Cesar hadn't seen two other women when we first started dating, as he'd said, but five, maybe more. There were tens of thousands of messages, explicit photos, and graphic videos, along with arranged meetups for sex. His notes were filled with information about each woman, including her name, age, number of children, and where they'd met. There were written scripts of conversations starters.

One of the women he'd been sexting had been his last ex-wife. She referred to him as *esposo* or husband in Spanish. He'd claimed he'd forgotten they were still married—another lie.

The text thread with Maria was the longest. Scattered among declarations of love, they counted down the days until they married. "I knew you would be my wife on December 25, 2015," he'd written. She'd responded with, "*Siiiii...*" and a heart emoji. Their phone calls often occurred before or after ours and lasted longer. A few weeks before we'd met online, they'd toured Mexico City. Time-stamped photos showed the two of them standing next to his mom and others with his sister. I hadn't been the first to meet his family, as he said. He'd lied again.

I kneaded my temples. Tamara was in the kitchen cooking lunch. "This is shocking. Utterly mind-blowing," I said.

"What?" She looked up.

"Nothing is true." I blew out a long breath as I massaged the back of my neck.

She gave a sad smile. "I'm sorry."

I'd married a chameleon—someone who took on the characteristics of others. All I saw was a carefully crafted illusion created to fool unsuspecting victims. And it had worked; I'd been tricked.

My eyes flew to Tamara's face. "I have to get back. Cesar has full access to my bank account."

"You do what you need to do. Just know I'm here, okay?" she said.

I texted Cesar to tell him I was coming home.

"When? I've got plans," he replied.

"8:30 a.m. tomorrow."

"Yeah," he said as though checking a calendar. "That works."

The next morning, he strolled towards me at the airport, straight-faced. There was no "welcome home" or hug. On his wrist was a new bracelet. The two loops twisted together to form a knot in the center of a leather band. The design resembled one of those old high school promise rings.

"Who got you the bracelet?" I asked.

"I bought it for myself." He touched it with a half-smile.

"Hmm..."

In the awkward silence on the drive home, I glanced at Cesar's profile several times, wavering between fear and outrage. He carried my luggage in without a word and dropped it at the foot of our bed.

Peering down at me, he said coolly, "I told you yesterday, I have plans. I'll see you later."

I went rigid. "With whom?"

"No one, Kerry." He spoke slowly as though spelling a difficult word to a child.

"I don't believe you."

With a shrug, he said, "Believe what you want," and walked out.

In a fury, I charged out of the condo after him. *What am I going to do if I catch up with him?* Several minutes behind, I raced across town on foot. *What if he's with another woman?* With a pounding heart, I considered the options. I could take photos as evidence or announce myself as the wife. Maybe slap his face? *Can I do this?* I'd never done something so terrifying. So bold.

I found our car parked a mile across town. Cesar sat nearby alone on a concrete step that overlooked the beach, drinking a smoothie. I scurried behind him, looking for a place to hide. When I turned around, both he and the vehicle were gone. The phone's GPS sharing app had been disabled as well. *This is ridiculous,* I thought.

On the long walk back, I struggled with what to do next. *Just leave,* I told myself. *It's clear we're over.* But I couldn't bear to go back to being alone and unloved. *Like he loves me now?* A derisive laugh escaped.

Cesar returned home after dark. "Did you follow me today?"

I looked up to meet his cold stare. "Yeah, I did," I said as though daring him.

"Tsk..." he walked away with a shake of his head.

Tension hung over us as we resumed running the rental business. Like slipping on pleasant-looking masks, we smiled at the incoming guests and made polite conversation over meals with his mother. We chatted about nothing, pretending everything was okay.

But the quiet restlessness ended a few days later. After another long workday, Cesar and I stopped for an early dinner. The restaurant was packed; its long tables were nearly full. We found a spot next to each other and sat down. An oscillating metal fan blew muggy air in my direction while a soccer game played on an old-fashioned TV on a nearby wall. The place roared with a cacophony of conversations.

Cesar leaned towards me. "My therapist brought up couple's counseling and wanted to know if I'd be willing to go."

I looked in surprise. "Oh?"

"He wanted to know why I'm hesitant."

"What did you say?" I asked, then added, "Sometimes couples find seeing a therapist scary like it might bring up taboo topics."

Cesar smiled brightly. "That's what my counselor said!"

"Do you think it's true?" I asked, careful to keep my face neutral despite a keen interest.

With hooded eyes, Cesar yanked back. I went rigid with alarm but took several bites of food, pretending not to notice. Neither of us spoke for several minutes. The tension mounted until I couldn't stand it.

"I'm sorry I upset you. I was trying to understand your viewpoint," I whispered.

"I can't believe you'd think such a thing of me!" he snapped.

I recoiled as though slapped. "What did you think I said?"

"You know what you said." His voice dripped with venom. "I can't believe you'd accuse me of such a thing!"

"What thing? I was trying to understand how you felt about couple's therapy."

Cesar narrowed his eyes and fell silent. Several more minutes passed.

A strange calmness replaced my earlier panic. This had gone on long enough. With a deep weariness, I leaned toward his ear. "You are clearly unhappy. This isn't good for either of us. We both deserve more." Marriage-ending words sat on the tip of my tongue, waiting. "I'm done." With that, I stood up and walked out.

On autopilot, the next several hours passed without notice. Cesar returned home after midnight. He turned off the lamp on his bed stand.

"Do you want a divorce?" I asked.

"Yeah, Kerry, I do," he said; his voice was tired.

"Okay." I turned off my light. *This is it–here's what I'd fought to avoid. We're finished.* I rolled over to sleep.

The next morning, we headed to our first appointment. In the car, I asked, "Do you want to talk about what's happening?" Worry stiffened my shoulders. Cesar liked to remind me he had never married me for the money. *He'll be fair,* I thought.

Without looking up, he said. "Let's wait until after this meeting."

Later that afternoon we sat down with a blank sheet of paper. I wrote across the top, "Divorce Agreement."

"What do you want, Cesar?" I stared at him from across the kitchen table and waited for him to say he wanted one of the cars or, maybe, a paid position.

In a neat column, he wrote our company's value and then divided it by two. "According to Mexican law, I'm entitled to half." He pointed to the bottom total. "That's what I'm owed," he said. "But I'll settle for less."

"You can't be serious? I funded this company with Brad's life insurance," I gasped.

"None of my divorces have been fair to me. Why should this be fair to you?" he said in a low voice. "I know my rights. Half of the assets belong to me, but I'll settle for roughly a third." He paused. "Or we can go to court," he said smugly.

The hair raised on the back of my neck. *He wants to go to court,* I thought. I'd seen how the law worked here; there'd be no sympathy for a wealthy American woman. Mexican law would favor a citizen's rights.

Through clenched teeth, I murmured, "Okay." Rage, like acid, churned my stomach.

"And I need some cash for Mamita's second surgery and our living expenses," he said. "It makes sense for Mamita not to move, so I'll stay here in the condo where I'm at until the end of the year."

My fingernails dug half-circles into my palms. Cesar knew he had me trapped. "Okay," I said.

He looked over the details of our agreement. "This looks good," he said and signed his name.

With my fingers blanched bloodless, I did the same.

Our marriage was over.

I stumbled blurry-eyed into the bedroom and dropped face-first on top of the bed. I'd been a fool to stay—foolish. I should have left when I first found out he'd been cheating.

This divorce agreement would leave me barely enough to live on. I'd have to sell off one of the properties to survive, but I'd lose more money between the commission fee and closing costs.

I punched in my mom's phone number.

"Kerry, I was just thinking about you," Mom said.

Hiccupping with tears, I blurted out, "We're getting a divorce."

"Oh? I'm sorry," she said. "Bad things seem to happen to the best of us."

My mind went vacate.

"You remember the Mahoneys, right? They are cousins to your cousins. Theresa, you know the one with multiple sclerosis?" she said. "She was found dead on the floor this morning. That poor family with young children..."

Like pulling on an imaginary cloak of invisibility, I listened politely while she droned on. After several more minutes, I interrupted, "Well, Mom, I gotta go."

"Okay, honey. I love you."

I tossed the phone and sobbed harder.

I texted a couple of women I'd met at church, "Who's the best divorce attorney in town?"

"I know someone who could help. He'd do anything you asked. Anything..." one of them responded. "Let's get together and talk... for drinks?"

I got a name of a second attorney from a realtor. I'd recognized the firm. They had done the work to incorporate my company. I made an appointment with their in-house divorce lawyer.

A few days later, I dropped, panting, into a chair, dripping wet with sweat to wait for my appointment. A large box of paperwork that I'd carried up three flights of stairs sat on the floor beside me. My blouse clung to my sticky back.

"Would you like some cold water?" the secretary asked.

"Thanks." I reached for the bottle.

The phone buzzed. "The attorney is ready to see you." She pointed in the direction of an open office.

A thin woman dressed in a dark-collared top and black pencil skirt met me. "Hello," she said with an outstretched hand. Her cool grip was firm. "Have a seat." A pile of papers lay in a neat stack on top of her desk. An eclectic mix of law books lined the shelves on one wall, and a floor-to-ceiling window gave a view of the road.

She folded her manicured hands. "How can I help you?"

"My husband wants a divorce. We co-own a vacation rental business that I funded." I pointed to the papers. "Here are copies of the financial statements."

She waved a hand. "Oh, that won't be necessary. The law is in this case is straightforward. The assets would be split." She paused to stare at me. "That is unless you can prove he's done something illegal."

"W-w-what?" I stuttered.

"Has he?"

"Has he what?" I asked.

"Done something illegal?" The intensity of her gaze cut right through me.

My head spun. "But I used my money!" I exclaimed.

"Doesn't matter," she said curtly. "Your business is jointly owned with your husband." She pinched her lips as though the issue was closed.

"But your firm set up the company!" I protested; my voice was strident. "I emailed one of your attorneys and asked about the ramifications of making him a partner. No one mentioned this." I glared defiantly.

"I don't know what to say to that." She shook her head. "How would you like me to proceed?" She blinked slowly.

My throat tightened as if Cesar's hand gripped it. Grabbing the box of papers, I stood. "I don't know. I'll have to think about this."

"Okay, let me know if this firm can help you."

I exited into the blinding midday sun. For a second, I was disoriented and dizzy from the heat. My head swam. On the trip home, other drivers weaved haphazardly around me as if traffic laws were optional. I gritted my teeth.

A petite blonde, ten years my junior, met me outside at her building's entrance. I'd seen her a few times at church. Clad only in a bikini, she wore her lengthy hair swept up into a messy ponytail. On her mouth was a trace of pink lipstick.

"I'm so glad you came!" she gushed. "Come, come, let's sit." She gestured toward the pool. She listened, nodding a few times as I filled her in. "You could buy your way out," she said. "Do you want help finding a different attorney?" She touched my arm sympathetically. "You can get about any kind of help if you're willing to pay." She gave me a knowing look. "I know someone who'd do whatever you wanted. You know what I mean, right?" She peered over her sunglasses.

"Anything?"

"Yeah, anything... this is Mexico. Cesar could be thrown into jail on souped-up charges... or, you know."

"Would you do that?"

"I don't know. I'm not the one losing the money."

"That's not the kind of person I want to be." I flopped back against the lounge chair. "Why does everything have to be so hard... or cruel?" I fought back the tears.

Since marrying Cesar, there'd been one problem or betrayal after another. This past year had taken a toll. My weight had ballooned, my knees and hips throbbed, and my gums bled when I brushed them. It felt like I'd aged ten years.

I exhaled a long sigh.

Cesar would be a persistent adversary. I'd seen him wear down business associates until they agreed to his terms. He would do the same with me. He wanted money.

All those years, Brad and I had scrimped and saved to pay off student loans and the mortgage. We drove used cars and camped in a twenty-year-old RV. For a long time, my wardrobe consisted of four pairs of shoes and a few nice clothes. We'd spent little on Christmas and birthday gifts. Brad and I made these sacrifices for a better retirement.

My fingers unconsciously curled to grip my phone as I clenched my jaw. I'd seen how Cesar spent his money. The cruises and trips he'd gone on to meet women. The money he'd used to pay for hotel rooms and flights. He might have stripped me of my dignity with his cheating, but there was no way I was going to let him have my money too.

As I lay against the chair in the summer heat, a vague outline of a plan began to emerge.

LIFE ALONE

"Study the past if you would define the future."
—Confucius

Early September, 2018

THE ADJUSTMENT TO single life in Mexico had gone easier than I'd expected. Just this past week, I'd ordered my prescription in Spanish and walked out of the small pharmacy with the correct change and a white bag containing the medicine.

Most nights I still cried myself to sleep, but my health showed signs of improvement. I'd even taken off a few unwanted pounds. The respite from the stress had been good for me.

I thought I'd seen the last of Cesar. But every Sunday morning, he would show up at my door.

"I'd like to take you out for breakfast," he'd say. I'd study him for signs of an ulterior motive. A refusal sat on the tip of my tongue, but

I knew I didn't dare if I wanted to avoid raising his suspicion. Those mornings we'd walk downtown, keeping several feet between us. Our conversations were stilted and kept to business. He'd watch me closely as though looking for signs of a double-cross. I suspected he was keeping tabs until the divorce paid out.

I wanted out of our divorce agreement, but my vague plans relied on Cesar. An impulsive, arrogant man, Cesar often took on more than he could handle. If I waited long enough, he would most likely mess up and need cash, providing me an opening to re-negotiate.

The plan was a rotten one with too many loose ends. Anything could go wrong. I'd lie in bed tossing and turning most nights while various loopholes and contingencies ran through my head. There were a few illegal options at my disposal. I could sell everything and move the money out of the country. Perhaps run away? Mexico's laws made the simplest things nearly impossible. I could do something shady.

No, no, no, I'd told myself.

Cesar's cheating about destroyed me, but this new ambush threatened to tear me apart. It had revealed a shocking lack of regard for my well-being. He didn't care if I had to go back to a job that had burnt me out or that there wasn't any money left for my children to inherit. In a few weeks' time, he had spent several thousand dollars on alcohol, gambling, and sex. If I didn't find a way out of this agreement, he'd do the same with the rest of Brad's legacy.

With dinner finished, I'd sat down to watch TV when there was a knock on the door. I opened it, expecting to see the doorman with a few packages.

"Hello, Gorgeous," Cesar said.

"Hi..." After swallowing hard, I forced a smile.

He leaned against the door frame. "I've been thinking about you lately." His eyes lingered on mine. "I'm going to visit my son and wondered if you'd consider accompanying me?" The familiar scent of his cologne filled the air. His body, only inches away, warmed mine.

"Oh?" His charisma weaved a mesmerizing spell. I was entranced, like a mouse charmed by the cobra's hypnotic dance. I eased back to get some distance from him.

"What do you think? Wanna come?"

Everything within me howled no. I smiled. "That's so sweet of you to think of me. Don't you think you'd have a better time going alone?"

He leaned closer. "Hey, I walked through a new development a few days back." His voice was a soft purr. "It'd be the perfect place for the two of us. I could see you and me living there."

My mouth went dry. "Really?" I batted my eyes to hide the shock. Cesar was lying. With access to his accounts, I'd seen the letter about this property along with the pictures of Maria's visit. The two of them had toured the condo a few days after our split and put down a deposit, most likely with plans to move in together.

"You thought of me?" I smiled while my gut twisted.

"Oh, Gorgeous, you would love it there!" He caressed my arm with a fingertip.

I resisted recoiling. *Sure, you were thinking of me while you were holding Maria's hand.* I itched to slap the smug look off his face. In the swirling rage, a deep need to be chosen swelled. I wanted to be loved. Loved more than any other woman, certainly more than Maria.

Remember who he is, I told myself and took a deep breath. What I'd learned these past few weeks had strengthened my resolve. Cesar's deceit extended much further than I could have ever imagined. His ruse wasn't working.

After we'd signed the terms of an informal divorce agreement a few weeks earlier, Cesar pressed me for the cash. "I can't wait, Kerry. I need it now."

Unable to think of a reason for a delay, I accompanied him to the bank that afternoon.

"Don't you think it makes the most sense to get separate accounts?" he asked. Sighing with frustration, I agreed but knew the bureaucratic process would take up much of the afternoon.

"Whose name will be on this account?" the slender bank manager asked. Her hands hovered above the keyboard while she waited.

"Mine." I let out a sigh.

"Any other?" She glanced in Cesar's direction.

"No, just mine." I began to cry. "I'm sorry, so sorry," I said.

"That's okay," she said. A look of understanding crossed her face. "Before we can activate this account, we'll need to interview you at your home."

I nodded, familiar with this banking step.

"When would you like to schedule this?" She waited.

Cesar huffed with frustration. "Is this really necessary? We've done this twice before." His tone was strident.

Turning to face him, she replied, "Yes, this is a part of the process. Would tomorrow afternoon work—say between one to five o'clock?"

The address on file was where Cesar would be staying until Christmas. Before answering her, I considered if I should change it. All my legal documents listed that particular condo as my home. This step would require hours standing in long lines for a temporary adjustment. But if I didn't go to that effort, I'd have to hang out at Cesar's residence and wait to be interviewed. I cocked an eyebrow at him.

"Yeah, whatever." He shrugged dismissively.

"That will work," I said to the bank manager.

"Okay, then expect someone to see you tomorrow afternoon."

"Sure." I wobbled as I rose to my feet like a defeated soldier leaving the battlefield.

On the walk to the car, Cesar avoided looking at me. "I'll let Mamita know you're coming, but I won't be around," he mumbled.

I exhaled a sigh of relief at this news.

The next day I entered the condo. The place was eerily quiet. Mamita didn't come out of her bedroom to greet me. It looked the way I'd left it with the same furniture and artwork I'd selected with care. This was to be our permanent home. I wandered about like a stranger, touching a few things before I settled in to wait.

The hours passed, but no one showed. As the appointment time came to a close, I called the bank to complain. The interviewer will be there tomorrow, they reassured me. I waited again the next day and the day after that for the bank representative until a week passed.

Cesar's mother and I avoided each other like two feral cats. She kept to the guest room while I waited in the master bedroom. Cesar's belongings were strewn across the top of the mattress. There were stacks of papers, an empty shoebox, several clothes hangers, and a couple of shorts. Day after day, the items never moved from their original positions.

For the first couple of days, I busied myself making copies of business papers. On the third day, I spied Cesar's tablet where it had been left in the middle of the bed's mess. With a glance in Mamita's direction, I reached for it. My heart raced as I opened Cesar's text messages.

Thumbnail images of women—some posed naked and others with flirty smiles—filled the screen. The most recent one was a pretty young woman about my sons' age. I recoiled in horror.

"Hello, sweetheart. What are your services?" Cesar had asked her in Spanish.

"I offer all types of sexual favors."

He's solicited a prostitute! The device slipped from my hand. *No way. There's no way.* For a long moment, I stared at nothing. Cesar liked to use an ugly slur when referring to sex workers.

The translation of the most recent conversation had begun with negotiation for sex and was sprinkled with terms of endearment. Earlier that morning, Cesar texted he was outside her house waiting. Throughout the rest of the day photos of the two of them grinning at various theme park locations downloaded. In one of them, she had kissed his cheek. He half-smiled with a flushed face.

"You better be embarrassed, you piece of shit," I cursed under my breath, then looked up for fear Mamita had heard me. The apartment remained still.

Then I saw Maria's name. Among the slew of messages and selfies were photos. Some had been taken at our favorite restaurant and others at our preferred beach. In each, Maria pressed her body against Cesar's, smiling radiantly. Then, I choked. In the next one, Cesar, Mamita, and Maria stood side by side, wearing big grins in front of a local beach sign.

I collapsed.

Maria had been here to visit, and Mamita knew.

Cesar had unscrupulously used everything I'd done or given him as an arsenal for his next conquest. And Mamita had been in on some of it, too.

Thread after thread of conversations with women he'd met at the local bars or had found through online ads filled the page. There were plenty of "I love you's," "my precious," and "baby." One woman had complained she was short on cash. Cesar had sent her a screenshot of a transfer receipt with an amount that exceeded what most restaurant wait staff earned in a month.

That was my money. I clenched my teeth. *You sent her my money. Brad's money.*

A chill swept over me. How much of the money I'd given him for Mamita's upcoming surgery was left? I logged into the account, and my eyes went wide. Over half was gone.

Cesar hadn't just betrayed me, but his mother as well.

I sat back, numb. Until then, monsters only lived on the pages of fairytales. They were the stuff of myths and nightmares. They didn't whiten their teeth, wear cologne, and open their wives' car doors. I'd been naive. So terribly gullible. But no longer, I vowed.

Then, my chest tightened at the next thought. *What will Cesar do when the money runs out?* Gasping for a breath, I surveyed the room for some imaginary means of escape. I was trapped.

The answer was obvious. He'd attempt to leverage me for more. I needed to take a stand—even if it meant battling him in the Mexican court system. But I'd never protected myself before—not with my childhood rapist, my parents, and not even Brad, who had dearly loved me. I wasn't even sure if I knew how.

Old or new feelings?

Old, very, very old.

Breathe...

I can't. I can't breathe.

Yes, you can. Breathe... You can get through this. It's going to be hard, but you can do it.

That evening Cesar arrived as I was leaving. He smiled. "I'd planned to make it a day out on the beach, but I never made it. I went to one of the local amusement parks, instead."

"Oh? Did you have a good time?" The photos of him and the young lady flashed through my mind.

"Yeah! You should go sometime! You'd love it."

"I'll keep that in mind," I nodded, playing along. *Oh no, I wouldn't*, I thought, *not after it's been tainted with you on the arms of some other woman.*

Cesar's bank account continued to dwindle at an alarming rate. Money was spent on local clubs, expensive steakhouses, and exotic tours. Only a fraction of what he'd been given for his mother's surgery remained.

Cesar leaned closer. His nearness pulled me back to the present. "So what do you think, Gorgeous? Will you go with me to see my son?"

His proximity was revolting, yet desire spread like molten lava.

Why this invitation? To see the son he'd used as a subterfuge to hide his cheating?

Steeling myself, I met his gaze. "No, I think it's best you go alone. You two need this time. I'd only be an intruder."

"You sure, Gorgeous?" He stroked my arm with the tip of his finger.

I shivered with revulsion and longing. "No... but thanks."

"Okay, if you're sure. But let me know if you change your mind," he said. He'd smiled big again, crinkling the corner of his eyes. He turned to leave, but not before I glimpsed anger flashing across his face.

24

CHOOSING

"Appear weak when you are strong, and strong when you are weak."
—Sun Tzu, *The Art of War*

Mid-September 2018

A T THE TOP of the phone's screen was the date. Cesar was likely on a flight home. A few weeks ago, the texts I'd found indicated he was in *full acting out mode* —a term mental health professionals used to describe an addictive binging. Cesar collected women like trophies. From time to time, he'd revisit a favorite the way someone would admire a memento. No doubt he'd stopped to see one or two of his old girlfriends on this trip—and probably the ex-wife he supposedly had forgotten he was married to until a few days before our wedding.

The past few days, I'd been thinking through why I stayed. Why I hadn't forced Cesar to choose between his addiction and a life with me.

In my family, my needs ranked low, if at all. My uncle was never reported because "we didn't want to upset Grandma." Dad saw the pastor for counseling but never considered I might need help too.

A few years later, my dad hired the same uncle who'd abused me as a farm laborer, and the attacks went from sexual to emotional. I was harassed at the family's breakfast table, on the bus coming home from school, or whenever he caught me around the farm.

"I got your hat!" My uncle yanked the new winter cap Grandma had knitted special off my head. It was a white crocheted cap with a matching white band. "Here's something I made. I thought of you when I was knitting it," she had said when she'd handed it to me a few days earlier.

"You want it? Come and get it!" My uncle held the hat high in the air and then pointed at a nearby neighbor kid. "Here, catch!" He threw it in a high arc. I jumped with my arms flailing as it passed over my head.

The neighbor kid caught it. Giggling, he waved it like a bull fighter's red cape. "Here, do you want it?" He dangled it close before jerking it away. I charged, feigning one direction then dodging in the other. My fingers now were only inches away from grabbing the corner.

My uncle cupped his hands like a mitt. "Throw it here!" he yelled at the kid. "C'mon! Right here." He danced on the soles of his feet like a heavyweight fighter.

The neighbor kid tossed it just before I could grab hold of it.

I skidded to a stop and watched it fly. Just then, the wind gusted; the cap stalled mid-air and fluttered to the ground, landing in the driveway's slush.

My uncle scooped it out of the muddy brown water, cackling. He held it out to me; thin drivel of muddy sludge dripped off one end. "Oops! Ahhh... too bad. You still want it?" he asked me.

Trying hard not to cry, I nodded.

Dad stepped out of the house's back door with his face pointed towards the barn. He gave a sharp whistle. "Let's go. Chores are waiting," he barked in our direction.

My uncle headed off without a backward glance.

I stared at the soggy mess in my hand. The hat was filthy. No amount of detergent or handwashing would ever rid the stains. Grandma's gift had been ruined.

This wasn't the first time something like that had happened. Over the years, my uncle played the same game with Grandma's other knitted gifts. Tears of rage stung my eyes. My safety and dignity had mattered less than the farm's need for help.

I'd learned my place—how to suffer quietly, to stay small, and not to ask for too much. My counselor had it right when she said, "Kerry, many of us fear abandonment. But for you, it hasn't been some vague threat but an everyday reality, and you're terrified it will happen again." Cesar hadn't been forced to choose because I feared he wouldn't pick me. But he *had* chosen; he had chosen himself.

There was a text notification from Cesar.

"Gorgeous, I've landed for a brief layover and will be home soon. I've been doing some thinking. Can we meet today?"

"No," I said aloud in the empty room. "No. I don't want to see you. Not ever again." I exhaled, then typed, "Okay, where?"

"How about that cafe around the corner? Say at 4:30?"

"Okay, I'll see you there," I wrote back with a shudder.

As I closed the app, an intense feeling came over me—a hunch or what some might call a spiritual prompting. In inaudible words, I heard, "Get ready. This is the moment you've been waiting for." I knew what it meant: an opportunity to make a play for the company was coming.

I dressed like I was meeting a date while plans ran through my head. After applying makeup, I stood back to look. The foundation looked blotchy from nervous sweat, and the rouge sat like two blurry-red circles on my blanched cheeks. Out of time, I grabbed my purse.

On the short walk to the coffee shop, my nerves jangled like a live wire with heightened senses. The nearby houses painted in too bright colors of oranges, yellows, and reds stabbed my eyes. The loud voices of salespeople hawking wares, the blasting music from the open bars, and the blaring gas truck's ad announcement that played on a repeat loop made my ears throb.

Could I do this? Fight for control? It was one thing to encourage counseling clients to practice assertiveness, but something entirely different when it came to myself. Challenging Cesar carried risks, and he wouldn't hesitate to retaliate. *Could he hurt me any worse?* I wondered. *Did I want to return to a relationship where I'd been discarded?*

Though scary to admit, the closest I'd known real love was the Bible description of God's love. I had no idea what it looked like between family and partners. Brad had loved me the best way he knew how, but his had been a self-centered love. His needs and priorities came first.

Could what I had felt for Cesar be love? Maybe. I didn't love or even like the angry, selfish man—him, I despised. It was the broken man I loved. The person I'd glimpsed who longed to do better and the scared boy who yearned to be seen.

Do I love myself? I shook my head no. I'd been waiting my whole life for an inner void to be filled. To be chosen so that I finally would know my worth.

Up ahead of me, the cafe's patio tables, shaded by matching green umbrellas, sat empty. Cesar was nowhere in sight.

I tugged the heavy glass door open when someone reached around from behind to grab it.

"Hello, Gorgeous." Cesar's breath warmed the back of my neck. I resisted flinching and instead turned to face him.

"Hello, Cesar, good to see you. Did you have a nice trip?" I gave a friendly smile.

"Let's get something to drink, and I'll tell you all about it," he said. We waited in awkward silence for the barista to make our drinks. Once seated in a secluded corner of the shop, I looked at Cesar expectantly. Since his arrival, the power had shifted: I had the upper hand.

He crossed his legs and gazed around the small store. For a moment, he seemed lost in thought. "I had a good trip. My son and I went to a football game." He waited a long moment. "On the way home, I had a lot of time to think—about my life. About how this past month has gone." He took a drink, then sat the cup down as if the clay mug was fragile. "I'm not doing well." He looked at his hands folded in his lap and then back up at me. "I'm sick, Kerry. This past month I've done things that have scared me."

"I know," I murmured.

Cesar's head jerked up. "You know?"

"I've seen the texts on your tablet, the emails, and the photos." After a moment, I added, "and your diminishing bank account." I fell silent, realizing I'd said too much. I should have let him go first to test his sincerity. Now I wouldn't know if this was a genuine plea or another deception.

Cesar's face grayed. "Well, my new lows have terrified me." He paused. "So, I'm here to ask a favor of you. I hope we can get back together, but I need help first. Would you consider running our business while I get treatment for my addiction?"

I swallowed hard. *He wants help?* No doubt he expected that I'd pay for it. I scrutinized him, careful to hide my reaction.

"I know it's a lot to ask, but I don't know what else to do," he said in a rush.

I leaned toward his ear. "I recently heard a powerful quote. The podcast host said she used to think her husband was a good guy who sometimes wore a monster mask, but realized he was a monster who sometimes wore a good guy mask." I bent closer. "That's you, Cesar. You're a monster who sometimes wears a good guy's mask." My body crackled with both fear and exhilaration. I'd never spoken so boldly before.

He dropped his head, then looked at me; his face grew paler. "I'm glad you know the truth."

This was the moment I'd been waiting for. The combination of his humility and neediness offered the leverage I needed. It was time to make a play.

I drew a deep breath. "About your request, I have two requirements. First, we select the treatment program together. It must include marital counseling. Second, you sign over your half of the company, making me the sole owner."

Cesar's face blanched, then turned a reddish-purple. He leaped to his feet and rushed for the nearest exit.

A powerful urge to chase after him swelled—to tell him I'd made a mistake and would take back these mandates if he would only love me.

Yet he had the gall to act like I'd wounded him? Since day one, all our efforts had been focused on him, from the very first psychological appointment to the intensive treatment program to this latest request for more help. What about me? At every turn, he had deceived and betrayed me. And now he was running out of money to cover his mother's second surgery. If there was a victim here, it was me.

Was this request genuine or another ploy? I sipped my coffee while I stared out the cafe's large window at the passing pedestrians. *What did it matter as long as I regained control?*

Cesar's frame darkened the restaurant's entrance. "Okay," he said as he sat back down. He blew out a long breath. "I agree to your terms."

"Great." I smiled. "I'll contact the attorney's office in the morning about making that change."

25

NOTHING'S REAL

"The liar's punishment is, not in the least that he is not believed, but that he cannot believe anyone else."
—George Bernard Shaw, *The Quintessence of Ibsenism*

Late September 2018

THE NEW ATTORNEY'S name was in the list of incoming emails. Since meeting with my old firm's in-house divorce legal counselor, I'd hired someone young and forward-thinking. In a short note, he'd asked a few more questions about the company's structure with a reminder to expect a draft in a few days. Closing the letter, I rubbed my neck. *How am I going to get Cesar's signature?*

I thought I'd won when I walked out of the coffee shop a week earlier. That I'd secured control, but I had declared victory too soon. Since then, the subject had become taboo, and an uneasiness warned Cesar had no intention of relinquishing his half.

Meanwhile, Mamita's second knee surgery was scheduled. "I'm leaving the doctor's office with Mamita. I just forwarded the fees for the next surgery along with the payment information," he texted. "It should be in your inbox."

I stifled my shock when I read the amount totaled at the bottom of the letter. Private medical care in Mexico didn't offer surgery on credit or loans. If Mamita was to be free of her wheelchair, this surgery had to be paid for in advance. Fighting tears, I cradled my head. The bill exceeded the combined annual salaries of Cesar's entire family. They would never be able to pay.

Refuse to transfer the money until he signs, I thought, but then reminded myself, *Cesar won't sign, you know that...* When it came to playing a game of chicken, Cesar was never the first to swerve. It wouldn't be his life he ruined, but Mamita's. *Had he banked on that? That I wouldn't have the stomach to hurt her?*

Mamita had traveled across the country based on a commitment I'd made to her, not Cesar. No one knew Cesar had spent the money earmarked for the surgery. If I refused to pay, she wouldn't be able to walk with a temporary block left in her knee joint.

This isn't your fault! Cesar's the one who's put her in this position. Just leave and never look back. You don't have to see her again. Besides, there's public insurance to fix this. If she went home, she'd have no car to get to the appointments and have to spend all day waiting to see the same incompetent doctors who'd damaged the knee. Did I want to be the kind of person who reneged? Cesar had gambled correctly that my heart was too big and that I wouldn't sacrifice my integrity.

I knew he was capable of betraying me, but I'd never dreamed he would put Mamita's health at risk. When he threatened not to attend her funeral, I figured it was the angry outburst of a hurt boy. He had shown such attentiveness—running her errands and buying her favorite brands of food. Following her surgery, he'd spent the night in the hospital's shoddy recliner should she need him.

He's a monster, I reminded myself. *He's admitted to it. And no one's safe, not even Mamita.*

I wasn't holding the winning cards as I'd thought; he was. I'd been played; Cesar had won this round. And with that, I sobbed.

Keep watch. He'll slip up again. With a shaky breath, I paid the bill.

Cesar interviewed the candidates on the shortlist of sexual addiction treatment programs. Looking defeated, he hung up the phone. "Another ninety-day residential program," he said. "And only for me. You wouldn't be allowed to come until the last weekend."

"Oh?" I said.

He shook his head. "Plus, that place's too expensive." He crossed its name off the list. "Only one left." With his eyebrows pulled together, he made the last call.

At the look of his solemn expression, I said, "So, no therapy for us as a couple?"

He shook his head. "Sorry, Gorgeous."

"What if we created our own sex addiction program?"

He fell silent.

"I know what's needed, plus it'd be way cheaper." *And maybe you'll be here to sign the corporate paperwork,* I added to myself.

"Yeah, let's take a closer look at that..." He stared off. "Gorgeous!" His face suddenly brightened. "Hey!" He nudged me. "You ready to take a trip to see our new grandbaby?"

I recognized this cue—the conversation was over. "Yep!" I grinned.

He grabbed the keys from the counter. Their sharp edges dragged across its wooden top. "Are we still on to see the new apartment tomorrow?" he asked.

Despite my dismay at his callous treatment of the furniture, I trained my eyes on him. "Uh-huh."

"You okay with me picking you up?" he asked.

"Sounds good."

The new place was located in a quiet neighborhood on the outskirts of town. A few folks from church lived nearby. I couldn't return to the condo. There'd been too many fights and too many lonely nights, and it sat too close to several sex clubs. The thought of returning there sickened me.

The next day, we pulled in front of a flat-roofed home constructed of cinder block. A young woman waited outside. Her long dark brunette hair swung loose across her back, reminiscent of Cesar's escorts. It glistened with flecks of reds in the sunlight. After a quick introduction, she unlocked the exterior gate while explaining the house's features in Spanish.

Cesar watched the ground, listening.

"Please," she said to both of us. "Look around."

A dank odor, common in this tropical climate, greeted us. A small couch and two armchairs faced a large-screen TV in the living room. Cesar's gaze swept over the agent. "Shall we check out the rest of the house, Gorgeous?"

She waved us towards the corridor. "*Si, por favor.*"

The musty smell grew stronger in the first bedroom. With the blackout shades pulled, the room was dark. Two twin-sized beds with matching comforters were pushed up against the walls.

The next room was the master bedroom. It faced an interior garden surrounded by a tall brick fence. In its center were a few flowering trees. I stepped out to admire the yard.

"Gorgeous, look! Two sinks," Cesar said from behind.

"Cool," I called out.

He moved beside me. "What do you think?"

"I like it," I whispered.

"Me too."

As we left the house, Cesar said to the agent, "We'll get a hold of you in the next couple of days to let you know our decision."

She handed him a business card. "Call if you think of any other questions." She slung her purse over her shoulder and left without glancing in my direction.

I stiffened as Cesar turned her card over before pocketing it. Once in the car, he said, "Here, you keep it, Gorgeous," and handed me the card. "You're more likely to be in touch with her." And then, he squeezed my hand. "Ready to go shopping for the new grandbaby?"

I smiled cautiously. In the early morning, we'd be leaving to visit Cesar's first grandchild, only a few weeks old.

Cesar pulled into the mall's parking lot when his phone rang. "Go ahead and hop out. I'll meet you inside." He frowned at the number displayed. "I got to take this, but I shouldn't be too long."

The mall's cavernous interior looked empty. Children's laughter reverberated down the long, tiled corridor. A couple of families strolled by with tired, lagging toddlers who whined.

I texted Cesar I'd be in the supermarket's baby section. The aisles were lined with colorful models of strollers, car seats, and playsets. I stroked a light pink blanket against my cheek.

Cesar rushed in from around the corner. "There you are, Gorgeous," he said, out of breath.

I held the blanket out. "Isn't this pretty? Do you think your daughter-in-law would like it?"

His eyes darted about. "Yeah, yeah, it's nice," he said off-handedly. "Gorgeous, ummm... there's something I need to tell you, and then I have a question."

"Ok..." My feet suddenly grew roots into the supermarket's floor.

"I didn't go to the office earlier like I said." He paused. "I drove to town instead. I gave one of the women I'd been seeing a ride to catch an early flight tomorrow."

My outstretched hand froze mid-air. "Oh..." Images of the two of them together alone in a hotel flashed through my mind.

"I just dropped her off," he said as though reading my mind. "Nothing happened."

"You told me all the women knew the relationship was over."

He threw his hands up. "I did!"

"Well, apparently not clear enough if she asked for a ride." My voice dripped with ice.

"Kerry, did you just call her?"

"Call who?"

"The woman. Did you call her?" he asked. "Someone called her room and asked for me by name." He took a step closer.

"Who?" I said, confused. "What are you talking about?"

His face darkened. "Well, you managed to find out a lot of other information. Maybe you knew about this too," he snarled.

"Know what, Cesar? I have no idea what you're talking about." I returned the gift to the shelf and walked away. Once around the corner, I dropped my head. *Breathe.* I told myself. *You know he's not to be trusted. Be careful; you still need his signature on the corporate papers.*

After getting my bearings, I noticed a rattle that had been a favorite of my kids above me. I grabbed it along with a few more items and found Cesar a few aisles over.

"What do you think of these?" I asked.

"Nice." His friendly smile was back. "I was looking at these baby care products and realized that they'd have to go carry-on." Then he took another look at me. "We both know how much you like to pack." He chuckled at my expense.

Seething, I played along. "Oh, you know me!" As we exited the store, the subject of the other woman was also left behind.

For the next few days, we pretended to be one big, happy family. Cesar and I held our new grandbaby, took his son and wife out shopping, and listened to their stories about being new parents. All too soon, we readied to head home.

Clouds drifted past my jet window as I considered Cesar's waffling behavior. Was he sincere about getting help, or was he up to something else? Any direct effort to remove him as a company partner was likely to be construed as an attack. Yet, I needed to be ready when the next opening came.

After angling my phone out of Cesar's line of sight, I saw he was engrossed in a movie. With trembling hands, I typed a short note to the attorney requesting a progress update. After another look in his direction, I pushed send.

"Everything okay, Gorgeous?" Cesar stared at me.

"Yep! Perfect." I gave a lazy smile while I tried to slow my racing heart.

"Just checking."

"I was thinking more about the sexual addiction treatment plan I proposed."

He closed his tablet. "What do you have in mind?"

With a slight tremble, I handed Cesar the phone opened to the detailed notes I'd prepared a few days earlier. I watched him read with a smug smile, knowing he wouldn't think to open my email or check my messages. No doubt this same tactic had been used on me countless times. Like a magician's sleight of hand, his attention had been misdirected while I cultivated trust.

"I like it. I think I'll add a few things, but it's great."

"Oh, good," I said.

Cesar took the idea and ran with it. Over the next couple of weeks, he interviewed several therapists and personal trainers, and slowly a treatment program schedule came together. The date he set to start arrived, and the sabbatical began.

As much as I wanted to shore up my shaky financial situation, a part of me still hoped he was sincerely trying. Over the past year, Cesar rarely followed through with most things. He'd found an AA sponsor and then didn't use the guy's support. Our joint calendar was littered with his proposed tasks and empty goals. These days he rarely went into the real estate office.

Chuck had tried to warn me about this. "Kerry, ignore what Cesar says and watch what he does. Lying is easy, but actions always speak the truth," he'd said. Despite Cesar's impressive efforts, I reminded myself it'd be a mistake to believe he was sincere.

26

CHARM

"As soon as you trust yourself, you will know how to live."
—Johann Wolfgang von Goethe

Early November 2018

THAT FALL WE settled into our new house. It was nearing dinner time when Cesar and Mamita returned from her latest doctor's appointment. It had been several weeks since she'd had the second surgery. She leaned against the walker, grinning.

Cesar's face shone. "Gorgeous, Mamita's doctor is thrilled. She can bend her knee much better than expected!"

I stepped out of the kitchen to greet them. "That's fantastic news!" I smiled. "Lasagna will be ready in thirty minutes."

Mamita wagged her finger and, in a commanding voice, said something in Spanish.

I stopped short, suddenly feeling like the kitchen help.

Cesar scowled at her. "Hush," he said before turning to me. "That's all right, Gorgeous. Mamita's in the mood for chicken. I'll run out and pick some up."

I looked down at the open cans of food and the greased dish. "You said it sounded great earlier."

"I know, but we've changed our minds," he answered, his voice soft.

Since the split, my relationship with Mamita had changed. She'd grown colder and more distant. I'd lost someone I'd considered an ally, but maybe she'd never been since she'd met Maria first, and they shared a culture. It was hard to tell what was real these days.

Later that night, Cesar cuddled close. After a moment of stillness, he asked, "Mamita wants to know why you don't like her."

My mouth dropped open. "Don't like her? What are you talking about?"

"She said you've been cold."

"Wait, wait, wait... Why isn't she talking to me about this? You don't need to be running interference."

"She said she doesn't know how to bring it up."

"That's her problem, not yours," I said. "And for the record? Nothing has changed on my side." I considered my next words. "You didn't help anything by going out as a family with Maria. Maybe Mamita has a guilty conscience."

His face flushed. "I forced her to do that, and she let me know she wasn't happy about it."

"That's her issue with you, not with me," I said.

Cesar frowned.

For the next few weeks, I went out of my way to speak to Mamita in halting Spanish. Sometimes she'd smile politely before looking away; other times, she'd give me a severe look and correct my pronunciation. Every morning, she'd make Cesar his favorite smoothie but leave no leftovers for me. Why the change? With her knee on the mend, did she no longer need me? Or had her inclusion in Cesar's betrayal ruined our fragile relationship? Whatever the reason, the previous camaraderie was gone. I'd become a nobody. *She'll be going home soon now that the surgeries are over,* I reminded myself.

Cesar had found an older, more experienced psychologist to replace Augusto. "He's too green. Doesn't know enough about sex addiction, like this new one. You'll like her, Gorgeous," Cesar said. "Her office overlooks a large garden. When I saw it, I thought of you."

Unhappy to hear the new therapist was a woman, I smiled weakly, "That's great."

"There's a coffee shop around the corner where you could wait," he said. "Why don't you come, and we'll make a day of it?" He patted my arm.

"Any progress on finding a male mentor?" I asked.

Cesar shook his head. "I emailed a couple of guys. So far, no replies."

"Well, let's hope something works out." I exhaled, frustrated. Cesar hadn't been able to find a candidate the previous year either. At first, he procrastinated and then claimed no one was qualified, despite meeting several men through Chuck's group. Although our home-grown sex addiction program was only a few weeks old, it hadn't been fully implemented. Cesar wasn't exercising, hadn't seen his fitness trainer, and hadn't returned to the AA meetings. Whenever there was any mention of this, he had a ready excuse.

Meanwhile, I joined all the online groups I could find for women in a relationship with a sex addict. Several groups were large. One boasted over a thousand members. As I told my story, the more experienced reminded me that we couldn't force our partner's recovery.

Cesar located an English-speaking psychologist for our couple's therapist. Mid-afternoon, we drove an hour into the city for our first appointment. The therapist's office was located in a small gated subdivision. A young security guard stood at attention beside a golden yellow wrought-iron fence.

"*¿Por qué están aquí?*" the young man asked.

"*Tenemos una cita con Verónica,*" Cesar replied.

The guard unlocked the bolt and chain with a sharp nod that resembled a salute. The metal links dropped with a loud clang against the post. He held the gate open. "*Verónica no está lista. Ella tiene una otra cita ahora. Por favor, esperen aquí,*" He pointed towards an overturned eight-gallon bucket that acted as a chair.

"Verónica is still with her other appointment," Cesar translated. "Go ahead and take a seat, Gorgeous."

"Standing feels good after the drive," I said.

"No, I'm fine. Please, Gorgeous."

With an exasperated huff, I sat on the bottom of the upside-down pail. The shaded stucco wall's coolness felt good against my hot back.

Cesar touched the sleeve of my arm. "Gorgeous," he said, pointing down the street. "I think that's Verónica's last client." A lone figure of a young woman strolled towards us. We began to walk in that direction, bypassing her.

At the end of the cul-de-sac, Cesar stopped to check the address listed on his phone, then knocked on the door of the corner house. A slender woman who looked to be ten years our junior opened it. "Are you Verónica?" he asked. "We're Cesar and Kerry."

"Yes!" she said with a smile that brightened her eyes. "Come in, come in!" With a sweep of her hand, she directed us into the small home office. Once situated, she asked in perfect English, "What brings you here today?"

Cesar and I glanced at each other. I listened near tears as he described the past year. Verónica quietly nodded here and there. Her glossy long black hair framed her pale face, swept back and forth with the head bobs.

Verónica's face was clear of make-up; she didn't need any with her natural beauty. Cesar liked to ask if I would have fallen in love with him if he'd been my client. I always gave the same answer, "No." I wouldn't have allowed myself to; romantic feelings for patients were off-limits.

He'd shake his head, confused. "Well, I would have fallen for you," he'd say as though that answer should change mine. He hadn't been as forthright with Chuck; why so with her? Was it because Verónica's slender figure and warm personality were exactly Cesar's type? Over the twenty years I saw patients, I must have heard thousands of stories. Everybody told a slanted version of the truth—some out of shame, others, guilt. Cesar was well practiced at deception. Though what he'd shared was familiar, how much of it was accurate?

He finished speaking and stared expectantly at Verónica.

"Thank you, Cesar. I'm sure that wasn't easy," she said before asking a few follow-up questions. Clients often retold troubling events adding a few new details as more was remembered. Cesar's answers reminded me of the written scripts I'd found on his phone backup. Had he rehearsed these too?

"Kerry, I'd love to hear your side," she said. There had been so many accusations and painful tales. Could I trust her? Would she be different than the other women who'd fallen for Cesar's charm?

The silence was deafening.

"Cesar, thanks for going first." I met his eyes. "You painted a fairly accurate picture. There's not much to add."

He squeezed my hand; his palm was clammy. Was he afraid?

I studied Verónica. "It's been a very tiring year. Beyond all imagining. But I love Cesar and want us to work." A part of that was true: I still loved the man I'd first met, but the person he'd become? No. Verónica hadn't earned my trust, so I told her what she'd expected to hear.

247

She tilted her head. "It's clear you two are taking this seriously." She paused. "Often childhood wounds drive us to reenact old patterns. By slowing down our communication, these can be disrupted enough so that you can find a better way to connect." She looked at each of us. "Are you interested?"

I nodded my head and heard Cesar say, "Yes, we are."

"Great, then let's agree to meet weekly."

As we stood to leave, a tiny flicker of hope appeared. Maybe this new type of treatment could help chisel away the damaged part of our relationship. Cesar bent to kiss her cheek farewell in the usual Mexican fashion.

My eyes widened. "I'm sorry, but in the States, it's inappropriate to kiss your therapist's cheek. I hope you're okay if I say goodbye this way." I held out my hand instead.

Verónica's eyebrows rose in surprise. "Oh, please do what's comfortable." She smiled warmly.

"I don't mean to be rude."

She shook her head. "No, no, thanks for telling me." She gave an appraising look. "And Kerry? Thanks for respecting yourself."

As we passed Verónica's office windows on the walk back to the car, Cesar wrapped his arm in mine, then stopped midway to kiss me. Though the gesture was sweet, I found the timing and the location suspicious. *Maybe this is real, but maybe not.* I told myself. *In time, I'll know.*

On the way out of town, I opened the email to find a slew of business-related letters waiting for a reply. I rolled my tense shoulders.

"What's wrong?" Cesar said.

"Oh, nothing, just stuff I got to take care of." My fingers flew over the phone's tiny keyboard as I typed a response to the first one.

"Hey, you don't mind if we stop at the mall, do you? I'd like to take a look at those sandals we saw last week."

The work pressed with urgency. If we stopped, I'd be busy until late evening. The appointment had taken a toll, and I was tired, but there'd be a high price if Cesar was denied. "Sure, that's fine." I sighed heavily.

He changed lanes for the mall with a satisfied look.

One of the emails was from the attorney. My heart picked up speed. *Dear Mrs. McAvoy, I hope everything is fine...* the lawyer had written. He'd outlined several changes I'd requested and ended the letter with, *Let's meet at 9 a.m. on Monday.*

Once parked in the mall's underground garage, we headed for the shoe store. Cesar walked at a clipped pace past the colorful storefronts that lined the mall's corridors and said nothing as though preoccupied. I struggled to keep up while I scrambled to think of a way to bring up Monday's appointment with the attorney. He made a beeline for the shop's display wall.

"Here they are," he said with relief as he picked up the sandals. He checked their fit in front of the floor-level mirror. "What do you think, Gorgeous?"

I stared at him and then at the shoes. *Doesn't he remember that I told him I didn't like them?* The glossy black straps reminded me of rubber tires, and the top etching looked like something a Roman gladiator might wear.

"They'll go great with your clothes," I replied cheerily. Was he trying to provoke me? Then I added, "You should buy them. They look good on you," and to myself said, *you asshole.*

Something was amiss. Since leaving Verónica's office, Cesar seemed to be playing some weird game of cat and mouse. Reminding myself of the unanswered attorney's email, I smiled sweetly. A few minutes later, bag in hand, we left the store.

"I'm glad you got those," I said, hoping to keep him in a good mood. He nodded.

"Hey, the attorney would like to see us Monday," I said casually. Cesar's face went blank. "What?"

"He wants to see us about the changes we've agreed to regarding the company's structure." I tensed.

"Okay..." he said, still playing dumb.

"Yeah, you know... what we agreed on," I replied, struggling to stay on the right side of a vague line between saying enough and saying too much.

"Okay..." he repeated.

"I got a letter from the attorney's office, and they requested we come on Monday," I said. "Is that okay?" I braced for his wrath.

"You know, Kerry, why does everything have to be about money with you?" he growled.

"We discussed this, Cesar." My voice rose.

"It's always the same with you." He shook his head. "Money..." He snorted in disgust.

I squirmed at this unfair attack. Hadn't I paid off his personal debt, covered his mother's surgeries, contributed all the business' seed money, and funded our lifestyle, including the shoes he was holding in his hands.

"Fine, we can do it another time." I fell silent. Just as I'd suspected, My leverage was gone. Any wrong move and I'd lose half of all the assets.

The drive home was charged with a thick tension that poisoned the car's interior. I'd begun to hate that small part of me that continued to yearn for our relationship to heal. She was weak—a scaredy-cat who feared living on her own. *You go on loving someone who doesn't love you back, and you'll go broke.* I warned myself. *Watch for another opportunity and grow some thicker skin.*

Later that night, Cesar watched videos in bed while I worked. It was nearing midnight when I finally brushed my teeth and washed my face. Cesar turned down the TV's volume but said nothing. Tired, I rolled onto my side to block the worst of its glare. I was changing—growing numb.

A few minutes later, I was fast asleep.

27

SELF DEFENSE

"If a man, who says he loves you, won't tell you the details of a private conversation between him and another woman, you can be sure he is not protecting your heart. He is protecting himself and the women he has feelings for. Wise women simply see things as they are, not as their low self-esteem allows."
—Shannon L. Adler

Early January 2019

OVER THE PAST few months, our rental business continued to grow with new contracts. Guests arrived and left nearly every day. Cesar supervised the cleaning crew and maintenance repairs while I handled reservations. My side of the job ballooned.

My sons visited over Christmas again, but the barrage of nonstop issues and unexpected errands disrupted our family time. Cesar and

I ran from one crisis to the next. We spent the early morning hours mopping up a bathroom leak on Christmas Eve. Instead of enjoying the holidays with family, we fielded questions, soothed disgruntled clients, and raced behind cleaning crews. Though my sons said nothing, I could sense their disappointment when I said goodbye at the airport.

With the start of the new year, Mamita's knee was healed enough for her to return home. As I said farewell to her, there was a palpable relief of being set free from one more stressor.

It had been another long day. I sat hunched over the laptop when Cesar walked in from the kitchen carrying a big bowl of hot popcorn and a tall glass of mineral water for me.

"Here you go, Gorgeous," he said. "I figured you need something to help to pick you up." Then, he plopped on the bed to watch a repeat of one of his favorites. "Gorgeous, I've been thinking," he said. "It's time I told Maria it's over."

I sat upright. Cesar had intimated he'd told her this months ago. "Oh?" My curiosity over being misled won out over anger.

"Ending the relationship is the right thing." Cesar stared down at his lap thoughtfully. "Would you be okay if I called now?"

Among my notes was a rough draft I'd started. I'd addressed it to Maria as a private journal exercise. She'd known of my existence but hadn't cared if she hurt me. Unsure how to heal, I tried to excise my rage with writing.

Cesar dialed her number. *"Bueno. Soy Cesar."* They chatted in Spanish for several minutes. I could hear a few of her soft replies from across the room. Nervousness interfered with my concentration, making my understanding of what was said blurr in and out.

"Adios, Maria," he said.

Her next words were crystal clear. *"Te amo, Cesar... te amo."* "I love you," she'd said. Friends and family used *"te quiero"* to express close affection. *"Te amo"* was reserved for lovers.

"Well, I did it. It's over," he said as he hung up. Expressionless, he resumed the show he'd been watching.

I sat baffled. The entire exchange had been weird. Who spent five-minutes chitchatting to cut off a relationship, and why offer me this glimpse?

"How are you feeling?" I asked.

"Good."

Still uneasy, I replied, "Okay."

Once finished with work, I returned to finish the letter I started to Maria. More words poured out.

"Gorgeous, are you ready to go to bed?" In the dark, Cesar pulled me against the warmth of his body. "You feeling better?" he asked in a tender voice.

I stared upward. "I'm not sure," I said slowly. "I heard her tell you she loves you." I held my breath for what he'd say next. Only a faint outline of his facial features was visible. His jet-black eyes grew small. He went still except for his breath.

"How did that make you feel?" I asked for the second time.

"I don't know," he said in a strangled voice.

"It must have been hard." I waited for a reply. When he didn't, I added, "Thanks for ending it." I squeezed him until his cheek was pressed against my face. His scent filled my nose. Cesar bent forward, bypassing my mouth, to kiss my forehead.

Maria's word replayed. The way she'd said "*Te amo*" had burrowed deep, like a haunting melody. I brought the subject up at the next session with my counselor, Lisa.

"Cesar took a big step," Lisa said.

"Yeah, it was," I replied. "Maria ending the call with 'I love you's?" My voice raised. "What the hell?" I fell silent for a moment, then added, "I've taken the liberty to write her."

Lisa cocked an eyebrow.

"No, no, I haven't done anything rash." I raised my hands in protest. She looked relieved. "Would you like to read it aloud?"

Dear Maria,

Now I know you and Cesar have had a long-standing relationship. It seems Cesar is only able to temporarily love the one he's with until that moment passes and he's with the next person. The effect of this is no actual loyalty or a genuine commitment to any woman. Not to you. Not to me.

I have also realized you have been duplicitous in this betrayal. Cesar wasn't the only one who hurt me. You did too. You knowingly took his calls and exchanged sentiments. I don't know what to say in response to this discovery.

You betrayed me and the concept of marriage when you declared your ongoing love for him.

It's disheartening to discover that there are women, such as yourself, who are willing to hurt others in the same way they have been hurt. I wanted to let you know I know. That I'm aware. I now know you are willing to take Cesar's leftovers rather than think enough of yourself to expect his whole heart.

I'm not looking for any response from you. In fact, please don't contact me. I hope you never experience this kind of relationship pain or act in such a way that it results in hurting another woman like this again.

"That's an amazing letter!" Lisa smiled.

"Really? I've considered sending it, but I wasn't sure."

"You should. As long as you don't get invested in her reaction."

"I thought you'd tell me to burn it or something." I chuckled.

I waited to tell Cesar about the letter until later that evening. As we lay beside one another in bed, his body went rigid.

"Why can't you find peace, Gorgeous?" His voice sounded tired. "What will it take for you to put this behind you?"

Put it behind me? Tears burned the back of my eyes. *There have been no apologies. Not even a recognition of what's happened.* "That may not be possible, Cesar."

"If emailing her will help, then send it," he said in a low, soft voice.

"Really? You're okay with me doing that?" I repeated.

"Yeah, I am."

But who I'm really furious with is you! I shuddered. That was a dangerous thought. Cesar had made it clear there was no room for my rage. Maria was an easier target—at least somebody would be held accountable.

Relieved, I opened my phone. "Done."

Cesar moved to kiss my forehead. This time I tipped my head, so our lips touched. He pulled back instead of deepening the peck.

"I miss you," I whispered. It had been nearly two weeks since we'd last been intimate. "It's been a while," I said softly.

He snuggled closer. "I'm tired, Gorgeous," he replied in a weary voice.

"I love you." Hidden in those words was a silent cry. A need for more. To be seen.

"I love you more," he whispered. "Get some sleep. Tomorrow's a busy day." And he kissed my forehead again.

Stupid... My heart pinched painfully. *That was dumb to ask.* Images of the chic escorts he'd pursued danced in my head. *You're fat. That's why he doesn't want you. Why would he want a cow like you when he can buy any 'body' he wants?* I'd read once that the least interested partner in a relationship was the one with the most power. That was Cesar. He was in control. *Detach, Kerry, take a big step back.*

The next morning, I woke to a note from Maria.

Hello, Kerry,

Well, we have two versions of the story. I understand perfectly what you are saying, and I don't want to get into finger-pointing or blaming. The picture and the idea that you have of me is your perception—so I'll respect it.

I'm not going to mention anything of the conversations between Cesar and myself.

How can I explain our story? I can't, except to say that it's love. All I can say is that I love him deeply. I want all the good things for you and will respect you and don't want to offend or judge you.

If you have any questions, feel free to ask.

-Maria

Confused, I re-read it. I'd expected Maria not to respond or maybe send an angry rebuttal, but to portray herself as the victim? Never.

In the middle of the letter, Maria had used the present tense to describe their relationship. Did she mean it was ongoing? Conjugating verb tenses was tricky for most bilingual speakers. I chalked it up to an innocent mistake.

That evening as we were driving home, I mentioned I'd heard from Maria.

"Ohhh?" Cesar stiffened. "What did she say?" I read the note aloud., "So, Gorgeous, what do you think?" he asked.

Angry tears dripped. "I hadn't expected this kind of a reaction. She doesn't understand what she's done. There's no remorse." I fell silent. "Honestly, if I had any idea this was what I'd hear, I'd never have contacted her." I looked away.

"Maria and I spoke about her being involved with a married man," Cesar said. "In the past, she's been critical of others but now finds it hard to resist the powerful feelings."

"I am sorry, but that's not a justification. What you two did was wrong—you've both betrayed me." I shot him a glare. "I saw the photos, Cesar. I know you took her to our favorite beach and restaurant. I've read the text messages of you two gushing over each other." My body lit on fire with rage. The past year of hurt exploded. "I can't believe what you've done. There's nothing special left about our relationship—you've ruined it," I said. "How could you?" I spat at him. "Fucking unbelievable," I said under my breath.

I glanced in his direction as the anger drained away, suddenly afraid.

Cesar stared at the road ahead of him; his jawline tensed. He said nothing for several long seconds. "I'm a sex addict, Kerry. I will be for the rest of my life," he said. "I'm very sorry I've made you feel how you do. You're going to have to decide if you can live with me." He spoke quietly but firmly.

My mouth dropped. *That's it? That's all there's to say? You're not sorry? Just sorry that I'm upset.* The scenery outside my window passed without my notice while I silently swore at him over and over.

Cesar had drawn a line. This was my problem, not his.

28

FOOLS & POWER

"Recognizing the truth about ourselves is the starting point of all change."
—Akiroq Brost

April 2019

HOW DID I *end up in this mess?* I rolled to look out at the patio. In the dusky light, the pink flowers that dotted the small tree were still visible. Tall grass bent over in an unsightly mess. Since we'd moved to this rental, Cesar hadn't bothered to mow. The once pretty yard had become overgrown. Its neglected state made it look forgotten—even unloved—a fitting metaphor for our marriage.

Little of this marriage resembled the one I'd had with Brad. Brad and I argued head-on with plenty of yelling and arms flapping. We'd swear and storm around the house, but things would get resolved— slowly and over time. Arguments with Cesar were quiet affairs. Divorce dangled above my head and would bring terrible financial loss. Cesar blew up at the slightest provocation and would tear out of the house to be gone for hours. After he left, I'd scream into a pillow, "I hate you! I hate you!"

I didn't bother to respond to the attorney's latest request to meet. The new corporate paperwork was ready, but it was obvious Cesar would never agree to sign. My leverage was gone.

I readied for bed, tired, after another long day of dealing with guests and staff. A few weeks ago, we'd begun to transition the company operations to another management team. This would result in a loss of revenue, but I needed a break.

My toothpaste in the sink was bloody red, the same as it had been for the past few weeks. Flossing hadn't helped. My urine had turned a cloudy tan, and frothy bubbles covered the top of the stool's water. One of my toenails fell off when I removed the polish. White lines covered my nail beds. I was falling apart in bits and pieces.

I crawled into bed next to Cesar. He sat in his usual spot with a bowl of popcorn. Dash-cam clips of car accidents played on the TV screen. He chuckled.

"Mind if I have some?" Even though I'd brushed my teeth, I reached for a handful.

"Sure." He nudged the bowl towards me and slipped his arm around my neck. I drooped and, like molasses sliding down the side of a jar, I nodded off.

I awoke, unsure of how much time had passed. The same clip played. Cesar munched loudly beside me. He moved forward to peek at his phone's screen, just out of my line of sight, and typed a few words. After hitting send, he flipped it over. I waited, pretending to sleep.

He turned his phone again, typed something, and spun it upside down. With a quick flick of his wrist, he checked for messages several more times. His movements were jerky. Nervous-like.

He moved the phone closer, and the screen moved into my view. Along the top banner was the thumbnail image of a familiar-looking dark-haired woman. My limbs went rigid, and the metallic taste of adrenaline filled my mouth.

Say something, I urged myself. *C'mon. Say something.* My parched tongue stuck. *Do something!* My muscles had locked. *Move. C'mon, you can do this.* From a distance, I heard myself say, "Who are you texting?"

Cesar jumped. "W-w-what?" he stuttered.

"You've been texting someone. Who is it?" My voice sounded calm, despite the violent trembling that had taken over my body.

"No one. I'm not texting anyone."

"Yes, you were. I saw you," I said. "You've been texting a woman. Who is it?"

"I don't know what you are talking about."

"You've been texting someone who looks like Maria."

"Yeah, okay!" he said in a huff. "I've been texting someone—my sister." He paused a beat. "We've been discussing Mamita." His voice was strident.

"Then, you won't mind me seeing the messages." I reached out for the device. Anger had created momentum.

"Yes, I do mind," Cesar said. "I'm not giving you the phone. In fact, I'm done talking about this." He turned off the TV and headed for the bathroom.

I called out, "We decided over a year ago that any kind of refusal is an admission of guilt. So, that means I'm going to have to think about what I'm going to do next." I joined him at the sink and, ignoring my shaky hands, took out my contacts. Then, without waiting for him, I went to sleep.

The next morning, I woke to Cesar's phone alarm.

With the curtains drawn, slivers of the morning sun shone around the edges of the window blind. Staring upward, I considered my options. With Cesar's stranglehold of the company, there were few.

He moved beside me. "Gorgeous, I'm sorry my texting last night upset you. That it made you feel bad." His voice was tender.

I rolled to look him square in the eye. "I didn't have a 'feeling' about you texting last night. I'm telling you what I saw," I said firmly. "It wasn't my interpretation of a situation but what I witnessed." I paused. "You were texting someone you weren't supposed to. Your refusal to let me see who confirms that."

Cesar went still. He huffed. "Okay, Gorgeous, if I tell who it was, do you promise not to get angry?"

Fuck you, I thought, but replied, "Okay."

"Yes, I was texting Maria."

"I want to see the messages." My newfound boldness was back. "C'mon, hand the phone over. I want to see what the two of you were talking about."

"I've deleted the messages." The sound of a satisfied smugness had crept into his voice.

"Why were you texting? You said you two were over!"

"You've been so upset over the email she sent you. I wanted to know why she couldn't tell you what you wanted to hear."

Couldn't tell me what I wanted to hear? I fell silent, figuring this needed to wait for our session with Verónica later that afternoon.

I texted one of my friends instead. "You up for a cup of coffee?"

A few minutes later, she answered, "Sure."

I got up to dress. Cesar had moved from the bed to the chair. "Hey, do you mind if I head into town? I'm going to meet Sara." I stared at him. "Just for an hour," I added.

He looked up from reading. "Sure, sounds fine, Gorgeous. Don't forget our appointment with Verónica."

It was a relief to be alone on the short drive into town. After parking, I grabbed my sunglasses and purse and walked the last few blocks. Sara had already arrived at the organic vegan restaurant. She sat against the back wall on the veranda. At the sight of me, she gave a quick wave, and then with a few strides of her long legs, she pulled me into a bear hug. Her baggy spaghetti-strapped cotton shift floated about her slender body. "So good to see you," she said in a strong British accent. "Come, I got two seats."

With an exhale, I dropped my purse on a small pole that looked like a miniature coat rack.

"How are you?" She checked me over like a mother hen.

"Oh, the usual. You know. Nothing is ever easy." I looked out across the street.

"Isn't that true!" she said.

Just then, a small dark-complected young man approached with a white apron tied around his waist and a small notepad in his hand. "*¿Que van a tomar?*" he said.

"What do you want to drink?" she translated and ordered herbal tea.

"Coffee," I said.

After the server left with our order, I asked, "What about you?" I suddenly was too tired to talk about the latest fight with Cesar.

Sara, though still a new friend, took the hint and filled me in on her new romantic relationship.

I gave her a wistful smile before looking away. *Would I know love like that again?* I wondered.

Pedestrians, mostly tourists, strolled past. A few sported beet-red chests with funny splotches of stark white skin. A bird whistled a shrill call from a neighboring tree. It was another muggy day.

Our drinks arrived.

Sara lifted her mug. "Cheers."

I tapped my cup of coffee to hers and grinned. "Hey, thanks so much for fitting in a quick coffee, or rather, tea. I needed this."

"No problem. Anytime. Seriously." Her eyes softened. "I understand what you're going through. No judgment, okay?"

"Thanks." I flashed an appreciative smile.

"I got the bill. You return the favor the next time?"

As she hugged me, I whispered into her hair, "This means a lot."

Cesar waited for me outside the house. "You ready to go, Gorgeous?"

On the hour-long trip into the city, all the earlier things left unsaid had erected a barrier. I turned on the radio to fill the quiet.

Back in Verónica's office, Cesar and I sat on her small loveseat with a slice of space between us.

With one eye raised, Verónica looked between the two of us. "Something going on?"

"Cesar was caught texting Maria last night. You know, the woman he's been seeing on the side. He supposedly called her two months ago to tell her it was over, but now he's been in touch with her." I sat back.

Verónica knitted her brows before she swiveled to Cesar. "You want to tell me what happened?"

"I fucked up," he said, his face blank.

"Okay..." Verónica paused to see if he would continue. When he didn't, she said, "What happened?"

"I did something dumb."

"Okay, what's going on?" she asked again.

"I made a stupid error. Something I'm not proud of." He clipped these words short and with impatience.

I tensed while I waited for what would come next. Maybe, finally, Cesar would be held accountable—something I had wanted for nearly two years.

Verónica nodded sympathetically. "What was going on, Cesar? Why contact Maria?"

"I'm not proud of it. It was dumb. I know that now, okay?" Cesar's voice rose and fell in a singsong whine that bordered on anger. I recognized this tone—he was preparing to bolt. I watched Verónica, curious about what she'd do next.

She turned towards me. "Kerry, how are you doing? That must have really hurt."

That's it? No more questions for him? The stack of pain and betrayals was so high I could no longer see over the top. Verónica had been my last hope. I burst into sobs.

Concern lined her face.

Cesar rocked me in his arms. With my head pressed against his shoulder, the blend of his sweat and cologne smelled sweet.

In brokenhearted sobs, I wept. This moment wasn't real. It was just another elaborate show put on as a distraction. Comfort was a subterfuge used to hide ulterior motives. For as long as I could remember, I'd had to live on guard with the ones I'd loved the most. The same people I'd relied on were also the ones who had betrayed me—Cesar, my uncle, my parents, my grandparents, and so on. Time and again, I'd been put in the terrible position of having to depend on someone who was both perpetrator and beloved.

The moment passed. I sat back on the couch.

Verónica smiled, pleased. "When trust has been broken like this, it needs to be rebuilt. I have an exercise I think might help." The session ended with the unfinished business of Cesar's contact with Maria left behind. As I had feared, Verónica had been immobilized by Cesar's charm. An unconscious desire to fawn had blinded her to his deception, along with the needs of our marriage. He had neutralized the effectiveness of counseling.

On the walk back to the car, I kept my head down, feeling bruised and defeated.

Cesar asked tentatively, "What did you think of the session?"

"Not good," I said, exhausted. Every part of my body hurt. My knees, back, and stomach ached nearly every day. The strain of living with someone I couldn't trust, even with the basics—such as having cash, being out with friends, or having time alone—was sickening me.

"I thought it went better than that," Cesar said with a pout.

"I'm just tired, Cesar." *Play it smart*, I reminded myself. *Until you have a plan of how you are going to get the company back, don't provoke him.*

29

FALLING

"He who knows others is wise; he who knows himself is enlightened."
—Lao Tzu

Late May 2019

I WAITED IN the idling car while Cesar turned over the last condo's keys to the new management team.

A few minutes later, he slid into the driver's seat. "Well, it's done, Gorgeous. We're no longer handling our business' operations." He exhaled loudly. "Ready to go home?"

I flashed a tight smile and watched the condo building recede in the rearview mirror. Running a company together hadn't given us a common purpose as I'd hoped. It hadn't even kept Cesar from chasing women.

"What are we going to do with ourselves?" I asked. That was a silly question. I planned to work on the unfinished manuscript. The more pressing concern was what Cesar was going to do with his free time.

"Maybe you can get back to writing," he said.

But you hadn't said what you're going to do? "How about we take a vacation? Maybe someplace different. Like Barbados?"

Sometimes weekend excursions gave me a taste of what we once had. Not every time, but often enough, a connection that had gone from daily life would appear. It was easy to blame its loss on Cesar's betrayals, but it was more than that. Lately, Cesar had begun to say, "What's wrong with me? Why don't I find my wife attractive?" Though this comment was cruel, it also was strangely affirming.

Turning the company over to another management team revealed a deeper problem. Our marriage had no core. Maybe there'd never been one; perhaps it had rotted. Whatever the cause, something was terribly wrong. Fear drove me to keep Cesar busy. Traveling, though unsustainable, seemed the simplest solution.

Did I still love Cesar? I feared him, desired him, distrusted him, and cared about him. Was I in love? No. Could I love him again if he worked hard to heal our damaged relationship? Maybe.

"I know of a special date we'll soon be celebrating." He grinned mischievously.

"A special date?" I asked. June was full of important dates, with Brad's death at the top. Then, there was my birthday. It was also when Cesar and I had gotten married, but Cesar's hookup with Maria over Fourth of July weekend had ruined that.

"Our second wedding anniversary!" He chuckled as though I'd forgotten.

I smiled sadly. "You're right. That's a good reason for a vacation."

"Sure... if there's the money."

With his mention of our finances, I spied an opening. My stomach tightened nervously. "If we're going to be making an international trip, let's wrap up stuff with the attorney first." Careful to keep my face neutral, I busied myself while I watched for his reaction.

Cesar curled his lips. "Gorgeous." He paused. "This topic makes me feel shitty. Why do you always have to go there? What is it with you and money?"

"I'm sorry I made you feel that way." I closed my mouth, unable to think of what else to say. *Shit, shit... what am I going to do?* When my mother was young, she used to trap muskrats to earn a few extra dollars. Occasionally, she'd find one of the metal contraptions empty except for an amputated limb. The animal had gnawed its leg off to escape. What was it going to cost me to get out of this situation?

Over the next few days, I quickly cobbled together travel plans instead of using the time to write. No further mention was made about the corporate restructuring.

Before we left for Barbados, my sister and niece flew in for a quick visit. We rented a small oceanfront condo an hour north of town. For those few days, we lounged on the beach and caught up. Cesar and I noticed several condos in the same complex for sale. Our current lease would be ending soon, and we hadn't decided where we'd move. On a whim, Cesar and I scheduled a walk-through.

The realtor first took us through the large fitness center, coffee shop, and massive rooftop lounge with an Olympic-sized pool. She took us to the condo next, and with a big smile, unlocked the front door. "Just wait until you see this."

We gasped. On the opposite wall was a bank of floor-to-ceiling windows with a view of the jungle. The rest of the place had the same attention to detail, from the large kitchen and pantry with a lazy-susan and pull-out drawers, a walk-in closet with a built-in shoe rack and a soaking tub. A wide balcony stretched the entire length of the condo with an extended overhang. Out beyond, the dark olive-green jungle went as far as the eye could see, broken by a few small bodies of water.

Cesar joined me. "What do you think, Gorgeous?"

"I love it, but we can't afford it." I shook my head. "Not unless we sell something." *Don't do this,* I warned myself. *You are already way over-exposed.*

"Don't you have your retirement fund?"

"Yeah, but there'd be a fight with my financial advisor. Plus, I'd have to pay steep penalties and taxes."

He snorted. "I'd never let something like that keep me from a good deal." He pointed to the corner. "I could see you sitting there on a lounge chair writing."

"Yeah, me too." I let out a loud sigh.

"Well, you know your finances better than I." He wandered back inside.

I stared at the view. Where was home? Since moving to Mexico, I'd raced from one location to the next. Each time I tried to settle, Cesar would taint the place with his cheating. *You can't make another purchase. This is ridiculous! You are going to bring more money into Mexico when you don't have complete control over what's here?* My jaw tightened. *But I need a home. Someplace safe.*

Clients often chased one thing after another, thinking the solution to their problems lay somewhere *out there.* It never worked. Wholeness couldn't be found in a better salary, the next new car, or having a baby. It didn't exist in external things; it had to be found within. I never dreamed while I listened to them that I had met myself. I'd been looking for a place to call *home*– something I'd briefly found with Brad.

On the drive back, Cesar shook his head wistfully. "Wasn't that place incredible? The developers thought of everything."

"I'm going to put one of our rentals up for sale so we can buy it."

Cesar smiled, satisfied. "You'll be so happy living there. I just know it."

The deal came together quickly, and a few days later, I signed the contract with plans to move in the fall. But instead of being excited, I felt worse.

In her last letter, Maria admitted to a kind of insanity. *How can I explain our story? I can't, except to say that it's love.* She'd been counting the months until Cesar and she married, only to have him wed me. Only a crazy person would pine for someone who had behaved so badly.

What does that make me? I'd taken Cesar back over and over. *Am I making the same mistake now?* An ancient restlessness to find *home* had been driving me. The Welch word, *hireath*, described it as a deep yearning for a place that couldn't be found. But I believed it did exist. Since Brad's death, I'd resumed a desperate hunt—hoping first to have found it in Cesar and now in this condo.

This isn't going to work; I've made a terrible mistake. I rubbed my aching jaw. *Can't go back out now.*

As we readied to leave for Barbados, I glanced over the upcoming itinerary. "Hey, we have a thirteen-hour overnight layover," I said. "Let's reserve a room near the airport."

"Is that necessary?"

"Do we really want to spend the night on the floor?"

"I've done it plenty," Cesar said. "When you factor in how long it takes to get through security, is going to a hotel worth it?"

"Yeah, maybe you're right," I said, not wanting to start the trip with an argument.

It was nearing midnight when we landed. The airport's restaurants and shops were shuttered. We located the business lounge on the second floor and checked in.

"Gorgeous, look! Two chairs!" Cesar pointed at a pair of plastic loungers with a rigid contour. I dropped my carry-on beside the farthest one. For the first two hours, I dozed to the sound of other travelers' light chatter. In the wee morning hours, the roar of an industrial vacuum grew nearer. A cleaning crew began to stack chairs, slamming one on top of another. Their metal feet clanged. My lower back throbbed from the chair's lack of cushioning. I turned restlessly.

Cesar shook my shoulder. "Gorgeous, we're being kicked out. C'mon, let's go." He grabbed our few belongings while I rose to my feet, stiff.

On the airport's main floor, some passengers slept on rows of empty chairs, and others littered the out-of-the-way corners.

Cesar pointed to a large column. "Gorgeous, I think that's our best bet."

Without saying a word, I sat down on the thin, dingy-brown carpet that had once been a light blue and rolled my jacket into a makeshift pillow. Finally, the glow of the early morning sun warmed the airport's interior. Sleeping passengers woke as new travelers arrived, and the place came alive.

"Shall we find an open restaurant?" Cesar said.

"Sounds good." On the walk to our departure gate, I struggled to keep up. "Is Panama City at high altitude?" I asked, panting.

"No... I think it's at sea level."

"Do you mind slowing down? My chest hurts."

"You're right; we should have gotten a hotel room last night. I'm sorry," he said. "We are almost there. Look, there's a restaurant."

I leaned against the booth's cushion to ease my backache while I caught my breath. After eating a large breakfast, Cesar and I boarded the plane. Like two kids, we took turns watching the scenery blur past as the jet picked up speed. The last time we had taken a trip like this was for our honeymoon. So much had changed in the past two years.

"This is it! We're officially on vacation!" Cesar squeezed my arm. "And soon, we'll celebrate our second anniversary." He grinned so hard that his squinted eyes shut.

Despite my sadness, I smiled back. There had been too much damage. So much had been irrevocably lost.

My stomach lurched sickeningly with liftoff. As we gained altitude, a heaviness in my chest returned. I squirmed, trying to get comfortable in the small seat. The rows of chairs ahead and behind me seemed to draw closer.

I heard Cesar snap a barf bag open. Earlier this spring, I salivated until mucus poured from my mouth. Like a rabid dog, spit spewed until I vomited into a grocery bag. I unbelted the jet's chair restraint. "I don't feel so good." Panic-stricken, I turned towards Cesar.

I came to staring at the bottom of the aisle chair. My body lay across the walkway. Passengers, who had cleared both sides of the row, peered over the top of nearby seats.

A bright light flashed across my eyes.

"Can you hear me?" a male voice said.

I blinked.

"What's her name?" he asked someone.

"Kerry. Her name is Kerry," Cesar said.

"Kerry, do you know where you are?" the man asked.

A blood pressure cuff pinched my arm. A soft hand held my other wrist. "Her pulse is fast and thready," a woman said.

The man drew close. "What did you eat for breakfast?"

An image of bacon and eggs flashed in my mind. "Uh-uh... hmm..." came out of my mouth.

"What did you eat?" he repeated.

I heard myself speak gibberish.

"Drink some orange juice."

I took a few swallows from a straw that had been placed in my mouth. My backside was warm and wet; I had peed. My face flushed hot.

"I'm a doctor," the man said. "Are you feeling better?"

"Yeah." The words flowed easier this time.

I met a few of the strangers' eyes that watched from above. "I wanna get up. I'm better now."

"Okay, but take it slow." The doctor helped pull me to my feet. I wobbled with dizziness.

"You're being moved to first-class," he said. With a tight grip, he guided me towards the front of the plane and then took the adjacent seat. Cesar arrived with our belongings.

The flight attendant bent close. "We have another two hours before we land in Barbados. Can you make it?" she asked. "The pilot has offered to land in Bogota, Colombia."

Still groggy, I steadied myself. "No, I'll be fine. Let's finish the trip."

"You sure, Gorgeous?" Cesar sounded concerned.

"I'll be okay." The last thing I wanted was to be stuck in another country with an unknown healthcare system.

Cesar touched my forearm. "You have to promise to see a doctor as soon as possible, though."

"I promise." I smiled to cover my irritation with his fussiness.

We were met on the tarmac with the flashing red lights of an ambulance. The plane emptied, leaving the crew and the two of us.

A paramedic entered the craft's cabin. "Mrs. McAvoy, I hear you've been ill," he asked. "How are you feeling now?" He took my blood pressure as he spoke.

"I'm doing better."

"The reading is normal, so I don't see the need for you to be taken to the hospital but be sure to follow up with an island clinic." He whirled to leave.

Cesar glared. "I'm not okay with this, Gorgeous."

"Can we get to the rental? Let's ask about a doctor once we're there. It's been a long day." I could hear the pitiful mewl in my voice. My heart raced with the effort to stand.

"I don't like this," Cesar grumbled.

We arrived at the vacation rental, the first stop of our three-legged trip. Our host opened the basement patio door to reveal a small studio. She brewed me a cup of homeopathic tea before leaving.

Once out of my soiled dress, I lay down. A cool breeze from the opened window tickled the hairs on the back of my arm. Crickets chirped nearby. There was a soft hum of voices. Most likely, Cesar and the homeowner were discussing my health. Within minutes, I fell fast asleep.

30

SOMETHING NEW

"Silent lies are more venomous than cruel truths..."
—Ben Oliveira

Early June 2019

THE NEXT MORNING, we overslept.

"There's no time to see a doctor," I said as I raced around the small studio collecting my things. "We need to check out."

"I don't like this, Gorgeous." While Cesar stuffed his belongings into the duffel bag, he kept stealing glances at me.

"I promised I'd see someone. Let's do it at the resort, all right?"

"Okay." He blew out an exasperated breath.

As we rushed around, I'd remember Cesar had confided when we first dated that he'd considered looking to match with a disabled person. Though an odd admission, I said nothing, figuring I didn't know him well enough. Had he meant he wanted someone easy to control? Did he hope it would be me?

A short time later, we arrived at the resort to be greeted by a bellhop. While Cesar pulled the luggage from the cab's trunk, I got my first view of the sprawling estate. White Grecian architecture and manicured lawns reminded me of our honeymoon stay two years earlier. Just as before, a young woman gave a tour across the large property, pointing out its amenities.

Much had changed since the last time. I was no longer the reeling widow trying to survive the loss of a spouse. Nor was I the confused new bride who had caught her husband watching porn on the honeymoon night. Something new but fragile had begun to grow within me. Was it enough? Did I possess the strength to battle Cesar for financial control?

If our marriage was a violin, we were strung too tight. After years of wishing I knew how to play, I'd taken lessons in my forties. One of the first things I'd learned was how to tune the instrument. Each string had a sweet spot where it would sing. Over-tighten the tuning pegs, and the strings would snap. We'd been strung too tight for too long. Something was about to break.

I used to wonder why domestic violence victims made an average of seven tries before they were finally able to leave a toxic relationship. Now I understood; they were afraid. Each time I imagined telling Cesar I was done, I'd freeze. *What if I'm making a mistake? Can I go it alone?* Two years of criticism, deceptions, and betrayals had eroded my self-esteem, and self-doubt had set in. What would it take for this to be over?

Our room was the last stop of the tour. Cesar asked the concierge for the location of the nearest medical center. He gave me a stern look. "You promised."

"Yeah, I know." His fussing was nothing more than a superficial show of goodwill. Like an Easter bunny's rich chocolate exterior, it hid a hollow interior.

The doctor, a middle-aged islander, greeted us with a warm handshake. "What seems to be the problem?" She listened to my chest before running a diagnostic test. "Everything checks out. Your heart rhythm is normal."

Cesar looked on, worried.

I buttoned my shirt. "I'm okay, Cesar. I'm better now."

He turned to the doctor. "What do you think?"

"I can't say what happened on the plane, but your wife is doing okay," she said. "I'd recommend a thorough check-up once you're back home, though."

"Did you hear that, Gorgeous?" He looked pointedly at me.

"Yeah, yeah..." I murmured.

The next week passed quietly. We spent most days poolside or on the beach. Dinners were long affairs; we chatted over drinks. A billiard table sat in one of the restaurants. While we waited for an open table, we played a game of pool, making up our own rules. Cesar pulled me into his arms each night to give my forehead a kiss. Neither of us made a move for more. I was worn out; the relationship was spent.

The appearance of sweetness was only skin deep. Cesar's temper flared quickly. He argued over the finer points of discussion and would sometimes refuse one of my suggestions. Lacking the energy, I ignored most of this. Whatever had caused the collapse on the plane had left me weak. Mild physical effort made my heart race. Instead of worrying about the bigger concerns, I rested. Our stay at the resort flew by, and soon, it was time to move to the last location.

Our taxi driver looked puzzled when he heard the address.

"Do you know where this is?" I asked.

"Yeah, yeah, no worries." But he stopped to check the map, made turn after turn, and backtracked several times.

Cesar scowled. "Gorgeous, contact the owner for better directions."

"I am, but she's not responding."

"Try calling, not texting," he said crossly.

"If she's not answering my texts, why would she pick up the phone?"
I showed the driver the map that came with the confirmation letter.
"Just give him your phone, Gorgeous."
Sighing, I did as Cesar asked.

A few minutes later, we were dropped off in front of a tiny cabin. The two-room loft, trimmed in yellow and white, looked like the advertised photos. Across a one-lane road was a cliff that overlooked the ocean. Waves pounded the craggy shoreline. There was a pungent smell of pine from the tall evergreens growing behind the house.

The driver pulled away, leaving three tall suitcases sitting on the edge of the bumpy roadway. I reached for the smallest.

"I got it, Gorgeous!" Cesar's voice was sharp. "You need to let me take care of stuff like this." I huffed but headed inside to look around. The home was tiny. The first floor was a kitchen that opened out onto a small porch that faced the quiet street. There were only a few of the usual cooking appliances—a microwave, a two-burner stove, and a mini-refrigerator.

A narrow staircase, with barely enough width for one person, led to the second-floor bedroom and the only bathroom. The double bed's gingham comforter and matching pillow shams were decorated in the same cheerful colors as the house's exterior.

Thinned-lipped, Cesar carried our bags up.

I bristled with the worsening tension. "Wanna cool off in the pool?" I asked, hoping this would alleviate his bad mood.

"Sure."

With the last of our stuff put away, we headed out. The pool was located at a nearby bungalow-style hotel. The sun baked the top of my head on the short walk, and my swimsuit stuck to my sweating back. I had slipped into the cool water when I noticed Cesar tugging on one of the lounge chairs embedded in the rocky soil. Red-faced, he gave it several more yanks, then threw his arms up into the air.

"What's wrong?" I asked.

He lifted his head to glare. "I want to move it somewhere else. Is that a problem for you?"

I wilted under the intensity of his stare.

"Why did you choose this place?" he said. "It's too small and doesn't even have a furnished kitchen. There's no coffee maker, sharp knives, and it's missing a full set of silverware," he growled. "I don't know what you were thinking."

For a moment, I was back in junior high, taking the bus home. The tail of my one-piece turtleneck shirt had come unsnapped at the crotch and was dangling out of the back of my pants. Kids pointed, laughing and jeering, as I rushed off. "I'm sorry, Cesar," I said in a small voice.

He gave up on the chair and joined me in the pool.

I reached out to pat his arm, hoping to soothe him. He recoiled like he'd touched something hot and then swam away.

I sat on the pool's lip and fought an urge to explain myself. "What's going on?"

"You don't think—that's your problem. You didn't take into consideration the most important details in picking out this place." Under his breath, he added, "I can't trust you to do even the most basic things."

I stared, open-mouthed, at this unfair attack. Suddenly, I wanted to get as far away as possible. I moved to the side of the pool. Three years of abuse flooded back. He'd criticized my driving, the way I did laundry, my housekeeping, and even how I'd hung my clothes. He'd broken my trust, hurt me, and betrayed me. I didn't even know how much of what he said was accurate. Since meeting him, I'd made too many concessions and allowances. I'd put up with the most atrocious behavior. Time and again, he'd had torn my heart into tiny pieces and then shat on it, yet I stuck around to let him do it again.

There was something else in the familiar swirling mix of fear and shame: outraged indignation. *I would never tolerate one of my sons being treated like this. Then, why is it okay for him to do it to me?*

And with that thought, something new was birthed. For the first time, I saw Cesar in a different light. I studied him as if he was a specimen under a microscope. No longer concerned about his bad mood, I swam a couple of laps before I hopped out to sit in the other lounge chair. In the dappled shade, I opened a book. After re-reading the same paragraph, I gave up and stared out at the sea. The waves called to me.

Without saying a word, I walked down. Sharp, jagged volcanic rocks lined the cliff edge. Twisted, misshapen monoliths jutted up to form a chaotic row. White-crested waves swelled until they crashed. A spray of water would shoot up into the sky where sunlight caught its droplets, setting the air aflame.

I stood on a ledge worn by the ocean's relentless beating. *This is what Cesar's doing to me. Soon I'll be nothing.* The same constant persistence was also a strength; the water had eroded the volcanic rock, yet the ocean remained unchanged. A quiet settled over me; I would survive whatever came next.

Cesar and I walked to the small hotel for dinner. Its shabby exterior looked misplaced, as though forgotten in time. The dining room was a covered patio with a view of the ocean. Picnic tables dotted the rough plank flooring and the surrounding lawn. After ordering, we waited for the sluggish server to bring us American-style burgers and a large plate of fries.

Stony-faced, Cesar sat across from me, mute. All around us, couples and families weaved back and forth merrily as they chatted. A nearby man nearly fell backward, clutching his belly and roaring with laughter.

As I stared at Cesar again, a haze lifted, and I saw our relationship, clear-eyed, for the first time. It was nothing more than an empty husk.

So many beautiful things were missing—the need for one another, the delight in being with one another, and the trust in one another. How could I have not seen this before? I had been tricked. Cesar's show of love had been nothing more than fool's gold.

My phone buzzed with a rare text from Kellin, my youngest. "Mom, you free? I need to run something past you."

My stomach dropped. "It's one of the kids. I got to take this."

Stepping outside, I dialed Kellin's number. "What's up?"

"It's Cameron. He hasn't eaten in days, and his breathing is weird." Kellin's voice trembled. "Mom, he doesn't know what day it is."

My heart leaped into my throat.

"Can he walk to the car?"

"Maybe.

"Get him to the ER right away, okay?" Taking a quick breath to calm me, I added, "Call me when you get there."

"Okay." He exhaled loudly.

"And Kellin? I'm coming home."

31

PRIORITIES

"Just as a snake sheds its skin, we must shed our past over and over again."
—Gautama Buddha

Early June 2019

W E FLEW OUT on the earliest flight the next morning. I received a text from Kellin midday that he heard the word "cancer" being used. For the rest of the trip, I cried as I stared out of the jet window at nothing.

It was midnight when we arrived at a hospital in downtown Austin. Cesar and I used the taxi's red taillights to pull the last of our luggage from its trunk. All day, I'd desperately wanted to be by my son's side, but now that I was here, I hung back, afraid. Seeing him would make the illness real. I looked up at the tall, illuminated structure and straightened to my full height.

"You ready, Gorgeous?" Cesar laid a hand on my shoulder.

Too overcome to speak, I took a steadying breath and then nodded.

The cavernous lobby was empty except for an older lady behind the Welcome Center's counter.

"Can I help you?" She smiled warmly.

I swallowed hard. "I'm here to see my son, Cameron. Cameron McAvoy." The familiar sound of her nails on the computer keyboard rooted me.

She looked up. "He's in Room 112. Go down the hallway to the north elevator bank. Get off at the first floor and make a left."

Her words ran together like gibberish. I stared helplessly at Cesar.

"I got it. Follow me."

Still lugging our suitcases, we found the doors marked Intensive Care Unit. A few pieces of large medical equipment lined the hallways. A young woman dressed in a blue nursing uniform intercepted us. She gave a quizzical look.

"I'm Cameron's mom," I said. "I just arrived."

"Nice to meet you. I'm his nurse." She waved us towards his room. "Go on in."

I parted the wall of curtains and entered another world. The room's only lighting was a small overhead lamp. Like a spotlight, it illuminated my son's sleeping body.

It had been six months since I'd last seen him. He'd lost weight. His prior thin frame now looked frail, and his face was gaunt. It was as if all his coloring had been leeched away. Pale blue venous lines traced across his waxy skin. A breathing tube hissed with escaping oxygen. An IV pole with several medicine bags stood like a skeletal tree, and a line snaked down its side to attach to his wrist. I picked up his lifeless hand. His skin was cold.

Tears dripped down my face. "Cameron, I'm here. Honey, it's Mom," I whispered.

His breathing paused and then resumed; his chest barely rose each time.

"He's been asleep all day."

I looked around to see who spoke.

From the far side, my youngest son leaned into the circle of light from where he had sat hidden. "Hi, Mom." He rose to his feet, stumbled across the room, and with his long arms wrapped me into a tight embrace.

Then, he took a step back and searched my eyes. "Mom, it's leukemia." His were haunted. He fell into my arms, the last of his strength spent. The familiarity of his hug made me sob harder. Here was someone who understood what had been lost when Brad died; what was at stake now.

A carousel of images of Cameron flashed through my mind—him as a baby, a toddler, a middle schooler, and a college graduate. Where was the robust man who'd hadn't been afraid to carve out a generous slice of life? The person lying in bed was nearly unrecognizable.

"The doctor said we'll know more tomorrow."

Helpless, I bent over the railing to kiss Cameron's forehead. His scent reminded me of the times he snuggled close as a tired, sweaty toddler.

Cesar shuffled uncomfortably by the doorway, clearly an outsider. I considered trying to include him for a second but decided his estrangement wasn't my problem.

We stayed a few more minutes before heading to Kellin's apartment. My mind raced during the silent ride. That night, I collapsed into bed, scared of what I might learn in the morning.

We were met by a clinic coordinator the next day. She pulled a chair close and sat down; her expression was serious. "Cameron has acute myeloid leukemia. That's all I can say now. Once his first round of treatment is finished, then we'll know more." She fell silent.

I stared, blank-faced, overwhelmed by all the unanswerable worries. How long has he had this disease? How did he get it? What kind of treatment will he need? What if it doesn't work? Can he be cured?

"Any questions?" she asked.

I shook my head. "Not right now."

Cameron slipped in and out of consciousness while a nurse dressed in a mask and a matching rubber gown and gloves carried in the first bag of medicine. Its iridescent neon-yellow color seemed to glow. She opened its double-layered packaging and started an IV that would run continuously for the next five days.

With the focus of my attention gone, Cesar floated between the guest lounge and Cameron's room. Most days, he sat head-down, engrossed with something on his phone.

Finally, the medical team of three specialists convened for our first consultation. After a brief introduction, the clinic coordinator spoke. "Treatment could take as long as eighteen months." She looked pointedly at me. "Cameron's going to need you the most when he's at home. That's when your part of his care is the most critical."

Eighteen months? I kept a straight face to hide my shock.

"There will be four to five rounds of treatment. Each time he will come to stay here." Her eyes never wavered from mine. "It's the five to six weeks between treatment rounds that are concerning. That's when he's the most fragile."

It was late that night when we arrived back at my sons' apartment. I started a list of things we'd need to turn Cameron's home office into a makeshift guest bedroom. An odd stillness of waiting surrounded me. Pregnant with fear, the most important questions couldn't be answered in this space. I'd have to live with not knowing if my son would live or die for months, maybe years. I knew this place—I'd been here before.

"I'm going to have to stay in Austin. You know that, right?"

"I know. It's where you're needed." Cesar paused. "Maybe being here is for the best."

I turned towards him. "Really? You'd be willing to move here?"

"Yeah, I've been thinking about it. Maybe I could find a job."

"That'd be great." I gave him a fleeting smile before I remembered all the broken promises.

As the first round of chemotherapy drew to a close, Cameron regained consciousness. "Please stay, Mom. Promise you won't leave." He clutched my hand.

"I promise, I'm not going anywhere." The days ran together in a terrible parody of the months I watched Brad fade away.

Cesar chauffeured me to and from the hospital but made no further mention of his plans. During those drives, he would complain. He bitched about the heavy traffic, the city's hot, dry weather, and the high cost of living. He was telling me he wouldn't be staying.

Two weeks later, Cameron was discharged. The first round of treatment had left him weak. Cesar helped him into the apartment. Dinner that night was pizza. As we ate around the kitchen island, there was cautious politeness instead of the usual friendly banter. The loss of hospital care had left us uneasy.

As I picked up the last of the paper plates, Cameron said, "Mom, I have a headache. Should I call the doctor?"

"Have you checked your temperature?" I asked.

"Yeah, it's normal."

Cesar spoke up. "How about I set the alarm so you can check on him during the night?"

"Sure, okay." Cameron's eyes flitted about the room.

"That's a good idea," I replied, though I knew I wouldn't be able to sleep. Cesar's offer gave me a convenient excuse to check his phone. He had been too reticent; alarm bells were ringing. "I'll sleep here on the couch next to Cameron in case he needs me."

"Okay, Gorgeous." Cesar tinkered with his phone. "The alarm is set to go off at two in the morning." Then he headed to the bedroom, taking it with him.

After helping Cameron settle in for the night, I tried to doze but woke like a new mom. Seeing the hour, I tiptoed into the guest room to turn off the phone alarm. Cesar was sprawled out on the bed and snoring softly. The phone lay near his head.

I keyed in the password, and the screen unlocked to an opened text conversation Cesar had been having with Maria. Outraged, I carried the device into the living room to translate the messages.

Maria first reminded Cesar to be sure to delete this chat. Suddenly Cesar's unflappable demeanor each time I'd snooped made sense.

Maria asked if he was happy. "Follow your inner voice," she wrote.

A master at deflection, he avoided her question to say he was more worried about Cameron. The irony of that claim wasn't lost on me. Our counselor, Chuck, warned me to watch what Cesar did, not what he said.

"After a few months of therapy, Cameron will be fine," Maria wrote.

"How do you know?"

"Because my sister had leukemia and recovered eight months later."

"But Cameron may need a bone marrow transplant," Cesar texted.

"That's the best, if possible. It'll make him strong again. Remember, he's got the advantage of age."

"I lost my dad, but not a son. Cameron's type of cancer is aggressive." Cesar wrote, "Kerry and I will probably have to stay in Austin, or at least Kerry will. Still, you and I will need to be careful now." He paused. "This will be a financial strain on both of us."

"Well, leukemia is bad, but with excellent care, it's curable. Stay positive."

"That's what I think, but I'm in a bind trying to support Kerry," Cesar said.

"Cameron's treatment is going to be costly. What concerns me is your half of the money will be spent to pay for his care, leaving you with nothing."

I stopped. Blood pounded in my temples. *His half of the money?* I re-read that sentence again. *His Half. Of. The. Money?* Horror was followed by fury.

The cold-bloodedness of their conversation mesmerized me. I read on.

She sent a screenshot of a nearby resort. "How about a weekend visit?"

"That's expensive!" he texted. "But I'd be happy anywhere, even at a roadside motel, as long as we're together." Then he asked, "Where's my kiss?"

She sent a photo of her lips puckered together as if blowing him a smooch.

Sickened, I tossed the phone. Beside me, Cameron slept. I watched the rise and fall of his chest as the implications of what I'd found slowly sunk in.

Cesar had been after the money all along.

32

TRUTH

"Man is not what he thinks he is, he is what he hides."
—André Malraux

Late June 2019

CESAR'S PHONE SAT beside me while I watched my sleeping
son. Cameron breathed softly; his dark eyelashes looked midnight
black against his ashen face, and his right hand had curled to rest
against his cheek.

The intensity of my love swelled, filling me until my skin strained
to contain it. I used to stare at his slumbering form cradled in my arms,
amazed at the miracle of this person birthed from my body. All the
sleepless nights I'd spent comforting him as he battled to breathe with
croup or cried with another ear infection had been a pittance to pay.

I'd barely endured losing Brad. Would I survive the loss of Cameron?

The casual tone of Cesar and Maria's conversation suggested that they had discussed the topic of my money many times. I was an obstacle—a nuisance that needed to be managed, used, or dealt with. I thought I'd seen depravity at its worst as a preschool-aged survivor of sexual assault, but Cesar's disregard for my wellbeing rivaled those rapes. We were over.

While I waited for him to wake, I wrote a few letters canceling several pieces of business, including the purchase of the new condo.

He stirred in the other room. I walked in and handed him his phone. "I know," I said in a flat voice.

"What?" His eyes went round.

"You've been texting Maria."

"I didn't send her kiss back," he said. "Did you see I asked her why she made that funny face?"

I snorted at this childish attempt at distraction. For the next few hours, we avoided each other. From the other room, I heard the sound of rustling. I entered the guest bedroom to find him packing.

"I have to leave, Gorgeous. This is getting to be too painful for me," he said. "Cameron's illness is bringing back memories of losing my dad." I had heard this story many times. Cesar and his dad had lost touch. When Cesar heard his father was ill, he flew down to see him but arrived too late.

I stared, incredulous, that he would use this pathetic excuse to walk out on my son and me. Only cowards fled in the middle of a crisis. But it was just another lie to add to the piles of all the other lies he'd told.

Cesar chitchatted as though this would be a brief trip on the drive to the airport. He waved goodbye with a promise to stay in touch. A few days later, the location-sharing app was disabled, and he rarely texted.

The first biopsy results arrived; Cameron's first round of treatments had failed. Cancer cells had been detected in his blood and bone marrow. He was admitted for the second round—something even more toxic.

It was late when I arrived home. After another long day at the hospital, I ached with fatigue. I threw a handful of bath salts into a tub of hot water and slipped in. As the heat eased my tense muscles, the phone dinged. It was a message from Cesar.

"Kerry, I saw my therapist today. It's time to face the truth," he wrote. "I think you already know that we are over. I'm unhappy and need to take some time to figure things out. To take a break from all relationships."

I chuckled at this bald-faced lie.

"Do you remember the original deal we made when we split up a year ago? That I would get a quarter of the business? I'm ready to sign over the company to you if we honor that agreement."

I snickered. This was the moment I'd been waiting for—I was back in control. Cesar always said the essential rule in negotiations was the first to mention money would lose; he had forgotten his advice.

"I'm sorry, but that deal is off," I texted.

"What? Wasn't that our agreement?"

"I've changed my mind."

There was a long pause. "So, what are you thinking?"

"All I know is that that deal is off the table," I smirked.

Once Cameron's second treatment was finished, I arranged a trip to Mexico to meet with the attorneys. I timed my arrival for when Cesar was out of town.

Our former apartment was quiet except for the sound of children's laughter from an open window. Our engagement photo sat on the living room mantle. The smell of buttered popcorn lingered in the kitchen. The same musty odor still permeated the extra bedroom. Cesar had left our bed neatly made. Business papers sat on the floor in a pile.

Dry-eyed, I looked at all the things that had defined this marriage—the snorkeling gear, the popcorn maker, my flip-flops, and our photos. I thought of all the tears I'd cried, clinging to something that never was. He had never loved me; our relationship had been a lie.

Brad's death had started something new within me. Cesar's duplicity had forged it into a type of rebirth. I had become someone wiser and stronger. I committed to never knowing this kind of betrayal again.

Soon, two large suitcases were filled with a few of my belongings. The rest were stuffed into large trash bags and dragged to the curb. I threw out several pairs of shoes, purses, the few gifts Cesar had bought me, all the clothing that reminded me of this marriage, and various memorabilia. The two garbage bins overflowed.

Workers on their way home stopped. "Are these for free?" they asked in Spanish.

"Take whatever you want." I waved towards the items and then walked away as strangers picked through the stuff like vultures.

Cesar arrived home later that night. In an eerie quiet, we watched a movie and ate popcorn before heading to bed. I let him pull me close to kiss my forehead. All the pretense of sexual desire was gone.

Neither of us mentioned the attorney's appointment scheduled for the next day. We tiptoed around the unsettled business—like landmines.

The next morning, we parked on the street outside the firm. It was still early.

"What are you thinking, Kerry?" Cesar spoke low.

"You can have the cash left in the bank, all the furnishings, and the car." This totaled to just over a third of what he'd requested.

He exhaled loudly and stared upward. "I'm not sure that's enough money to live on for a couple of years."

I stifled a gasp with a reminder he could take me to court. "What do you want, Cesar?"

"In addition to that, I want half the company's net profit for one year." He scribbled on a notepad. "No, make it for the next two years."

Seething, I replied flatly, "Okay."

"And I want that added as an addendum."

Once again cornered, I nodded.

The law office's waiting room was bare except for a few chairs. A well-dressed man who appeared too young to be an attorney invited us into a conference room. He pushed triplicates of a document across the table.

"Here are copies of the final agreement to change the corporation's structure. All the shares currently held by Mr. Morales will transfer to Mrs. McAvoy," he said. "Do you both understand and accept these terms?"

I nodded.

"Yes," Cesar said.

"Mr. Morales, please initial each page and sign at the bottom of the last." The attorney held out a spare pen.

Cesar signed his name with a flourish.

The attorney then slid the paperwork to me. "Mrs. McAvoy?"

I added my signature next to Cesar's.

The young man lined the documents into a neat stack. "Mr. Morales, with this change now in effect, you are no longer a shareholder." He looked straight at Cesar. "Therefore, you cannot be in attendance for the rest of the meeting." He paused. "Please leave the room."

Cesar's mouth fell ajar. "But... but we haven't finished the last piece of business." He turned towards me. "Kerry, you agreed to add that I would get half of the rental income for the next two years!" he stammered, red-faced.

"You cannot be here. Please leave," the attorney repeated, this time firmer.

Cesar whirled. "Kerry, I told you we should have started with that addition first!"

Blank-faced, the attorney watched, unmoved.

Cesar stood. "We're out of time if you plan to catch the flight back to Austin. You coming?" He threw me one more glare before he charged out.

I sat transfixed. Never could I have imagined such providential help. Not like this. The rigidity of Mexican law had cut my losses. I'd never felt so grateful for the country's bureaucratic stringency.

The attorney looked on dispassionately while we finished up the last details. The final addendum granting Cesar two years of the company profits was never finalized. I stood to leave and shook the attorney's hand, thanking him for his help. He acted confused. He'd simply been doing his job.

Cesar waited in the idling car. I slid in but said nothing. After how he treated me for the past three years, I owed him nothing, not even an explanation.

We sat stiffly side by side on the trip to Austin and kept the conversation casual. There was no need to pretend. We were no longer partners, colleagues, or even friends.

A few weeks later, he flew in again, this time to sign the divorce papers. I parked at a nearby playground not far from the airport. I licked my lips nervously and looked around. The lot was empty. Meeting him alone hadn't been a smart idea.

Cesar studied the divorce papers as though unsure.

"What's the issue? We no longer have any joint accounts or properties."

"I want you to promise that you'll uphold your end of the bargain. That you'll give me half of the business' income for the next two years." He stuck out his hand. "Promise."

I stared at the offered handshake. This man had lied, cheated, and betrayed to maintain every advantage. Now, he was pressing for money that wasn't his.

He leaned near my ear to whisper, "Don't forget, you don't want to make me angry." I recognized these words. One of the sex workers he hired had sent him the same message when she'd tried to extort him for money and then threatened to kill him.

Cesar had finally dropped the guise of a good guy and revealed his true self—a predator. Since our first meeting, the signs had been there, but I'd mistaken fear for attraction. I was alone in the park, and in this car, with a dangerous man—a monster.

I shook his hand. My divorce was final a few weeks later. Cesar received nothing further from me.

33

ENOUGH

"Sometimes our enemies are [disguised] as family and friends. You must forgive yourself for having chosen to trust those people who don't care about your life and seek nothing but failure for you. Stop wasting your precious time in trying to make those people see you, understand you, respect you, value you and love you... Enjoy life by surrounding yourself with those who inspire you and truly demonstrate their love for you."
—Jesus Apolinaris

July 2021

A T THE SOUND of a knock, I ran to my one-bedroom apartment's front door; Cameron and Kellin entered.

Cameron bent to slip off his shoes. Straightening, he smiled softly as our eyes met. I could barely contain my joy.

"Hi, Mom," he said.

Every visit, the same thought has gone through my mind. *He's here, alive, and healthy!* I hugged him, gushing, "So good to see you!"

"Hey," Kellin shyly smiled as he scooted past to set a white takeout bag on the counter.

"How's your week been going?" I asked them both.

"Good, but long," Cameron said.

"Same," Kellin said.

"So, what movie are we watching tonight?" I asked.

"There are a couple of options." Kellin listed a few details about each.

As the movie credits finished, I peeked at both men. The past six years had brought so many changes—hardships, pain, and growth.

Brad had been the family hub. We'd built our connection to each other on the relationship with him. When he died, we lost more than a husband, friend, and father, we'd lost what had tied us together. Once he was gone, we rarely reached out. My phone and text messages went unanswered. Silence plagued most holidays; many birthdays and Mother's Days went unremembered. Except for Cameron and Kellin's friendship, we'd lost touch. Grief had walled us off from each other— alone and hurting.

Shortly after the start of the COVID-19 pandemic, Cameron, Kellin, and I got together to celebrate Kellin's birthday. As we wrapped up the evening, Kellin said, "This has been fun. We should make it a regular thing."

For fear of appearing overly eager, I grabbed a few dirty dishes from the table. *Please, please, please...* I had thought as I busied myself.

"Yeah, I agree. Now that I can only meet up with friends online, it's gotten pretty lonely." Cameron walked in behind me with another stack of plates. "What if we did this once a week?" he said. "Maybe Fridays?"

"I'm game," I said casually.

For years I'd watched other mothers nurture friendships with their adult sons and daughters. I'd longed for something similar but feared it wasn't to be. At the finish of Cesar's and my marriage, I'd moved into the same apartment complex as my sons. While Cameron underwent treatment, I'd stayed close. He had to be rushed to the ER twice and spent weeks in the ICU. During that terrible time, I'd sat by his bedside, driven him to appointments, and offered moral support. Eight months later, his chemotherapy finished.

My sons gently let me know that my once helpful presence had become stifling. At their request, I backed off, limited my visits, and barely texted.

The following week, the three of us agreed to meet. And soon our Friday visits or what we called "a dinner and a movie" became a tradition. These weekly get-togethers have done more than entertain us; we have found our way back, this time as adults. With Devon's plans to move to the Austin area, we will soon complete the new family constellation. Brad will always be missed, but we have finally become whole again.

"Fascinating movie," I looked over at Kellin. "Great pick."

He smiled. "Thanks."

"Hey, I wanted to let you know I've listed the Mexican business for sale."

"Okay," Cameron glanced in my direction. Since his treatments had finished, his face had gotten fuller and gained color. "How does that make you feel? Like you're closing a chapter?"

"It's weird," I said. "Maybe sad?" I blinked fast at the stinging in my eyes. "Letting this go is an ending." I gulped, then burst into tears. "I feel stupid, you know?" With a quivering chin, I broke into sobs. "How could I have not known I'd met a monster?" I gasped.

Cameron placed his hands on my shoulder. "It's okay, Mom. You didn't know."

"I trusted Cesar, you know? And look at what it's cost me." I gazed up at both men. "You must think I've been an idiot." Then I wailed, "I'm so ashamed."

With a flushed face, Kellin stared at his lap but said nothing.

Cameron patted me; his hand warmed my back. "No, no, we don't, Mom. Not at all," he whispered. "If there is any blame here, it belongs to Cesar. He used your trust against you." He paused. "You did nothing wrong," he said firmly.

"Really? You don't blame me?" I glanced first at Cameron, then at Kellin.

Kellin, his face a rigid mask of anger, shook his head no.

"No, we don't," Cameron said softly.

"I thought you did," I said, wiping my eyes.

For months, I'd danced around business-related issues for fear such talk would upset my sons. The topic of Cesar had become taboo. I blamed myself for rushing into marriage, and I figured others did too. Everything related to that marriage had turned into an unmentionable. To learn my sons held a different perspective surprised me, and I moved closer to forgiving myself.

A podcast about dating provided the final piece of healing. I'd been running errands when I stumbled onto a new show and decided to give it a listen.

A doctor shared he'd been married four times—two of the wives had died. "I was young when I lost Cathy—still in my twenties. Although it was a tragedy to lose her, Kristen's death was something altogether different. She and I had been married twenty years," he said. "After losing her, I'd become desperate to fill the hole she'd left. I wanted to find someone who would slide into that empty slot so I could resume the life we'd had."

I had done the same thing. After spending my entire adulthood with Brad, I had no clue how to be single. His death had thrown me into crisis, and I had frantically wanted to find someone who would pick up where Brad had left off.

The doctor closed the interview by saying this strategy hadn't worked. He divorced soon after.

It hadn't for me either. I sat in the parked car alone and wept bitterly.

The COVID-19 quarantine had given me the space to figure out some things—what it means to be just Kerry. Most days, I've stared out my patio window and written. Life has been peaceful. I've missed the companionship and romantic love. Single life, though, has taught me a few overdue life lessons. I know now that I am enough, never to give away too much of myself, and that contentment is a choice.

EPILOGUE

"A truth is, unless you let go, unless you forgive yourself, unless you forgive the situation, unless you realize that the situation is over, you cannot move forward."
—Steve Maraboli, *Unapologetically You: Reflections on Life and the Human Experience*

August 2021

IT'S BEEN OVER a year since I've last heard from Cesar. He'd finally gotten around to transferring the car's title and sent an email for a copy of the sale's invoice. The cordial letter ended with a request for a large sum of money. He claimed to be broke, unable to find a job in his field, and wanted to move back to the US—a doubtful story since I'd seen what appeared to be his and Maria's engagement photos. My refusal was met with a vitriolic second letter.

It began:

Poor Kerry, Oh Kerry... you always the victim [sic]. I'd come in a *humble way... When do I [sic] ever refuse to help?* Yet, you (Kerry) had come with *a wrathful vendetta with a personal attack.*

Then ended:

Stop playing the victim card.
Kerry, I will always be grateful for the time that I met you and the time we was [sic] *together. I discover(ed) and accepted my addiction during our marriage, although not a very proud moment but it has been a different direction in my life, for that, I am very thankful.*
Wish you well, Kerry
Cesar

In writing this book, I reviewed Cesar's text messages, photos, videos, and audio clips. Three of his four ex-wives were interviewed. Two eagerly agreed. Their stories were oddly similar. They described falling in love with a dashing man. He'd made grand romantic gestures, only to withdraw or disappear for extended periods. This vacillating reward and punishment cycle, also known as a *variable rate of reward*, created an addiction based on fear. As their relationships matured, so did the frequency of Cesar's mercurial mood shifts, extended absences, verbal abuse, and rampant cheating.

Cesar's first wife still lives in Mexico, where she raised his oldest child alone. He claimed she'd fled the marriage, stealing the baby from him, to escape to parts unknown. She said he'd gotten in trouble at work and left the country to avoid legal problems, leaving her and the new baby, struggling with a physical ailment, behind.

Cesar met an American woman next; they married quickly and conceived one child. Their relationship lasted the longest—for seventeen years. She drifted from my questions to tell rambling stories, as though the conversation was occurring for her own reasons but verified a few essential things.

"Didn't Cesar lose a bunch of his retirement money on a Ponzi scheme?" I asked the second ex-wife.

"Retirement money... what are you talking about?" She snorted. "You'd have to keep a job first. Every year or so, Cesar would do something stupid at work and lose his." She paused. "Did he abuse you?" she asked.

"Like how?" I replied.

"Hit you."

"No..."

"You're lucky."

"Did that happen to you?" I asked. She didn't answer.

I tried to reach her a few days later to ask some follow-up questions. My phone calls and text messages went unanswered.

I messaged the third wife about an interview but didn't hear from her until nearly six months later. My earlier letter had gotten lost. She responded with interest. I knew very little about her except that she was well-educated, eleven years older than him, and their marriage lasted less than a year. Cesar claimed she'd honored her friendships over her commitment to him.

A soft-spoken woman answered my phone call. Little of her description matched Cesar's yet eerily resembled our marriage. Cesar worked long hours and took frequent business trips. On an extended one, he'd forgotten to leave the name and phone number of where he'd be staying in case of an emergency. Unable to reach him, she called his travel partner for the hotel's name.

She paused. "His colleague acted confused, and then after a long silence said, 'I thought he was with you.'" She waited for a beat. "I kicked him out. Moved all his stuff out to the curb. I didn't even bother to pick him up from the airport." She stifled a chuckle. "He came home from that trip to nothing and nowhere to go."

She had done what I couldn't—left the marriage. Cesar's panic attack that morning in the honeymoon resort suddenly made more sense. He hadn't been afraid of losing me, as I'd thought; he feared he'd found himself in the same predicament as before—going home to nothing and nowhere to go.

It was what she said next that sent me reeling.

"I think Cesar was poisoning me."

"W-what?" I stuttered.

"During the marriage, I got really sick." Then she repeated her assertion, "I think he was poisoning me."

"Do you know that for sure?"

"No, but it's the only thing that makes sense."

Utterly shocked, I ended the call.

I had feared the same thing. Since my arrival to Mexico two years earlier, I'd been slowly getting sicker. Shortly before the trip to Barbados, I had noticed white lines across all my fingernails. Then a toenail fell off.

Heavy metal, mainly arsenic—an odorless, tasteless chemical—was readily available in that country. *Arsenicum Album*, a homeopathic remedy, was sold as dissolvable tabs. One of its tell-tale signs is Mees lines, a white discoloration on the back of fingernails that run parallel to the nail bed.

I called her a few weeks later to ask a couple more questions. She didn't pick up but texted a brief response. Though she didn't recant the initial story, her earlier enthusiasm to talk had disappeared. Had she feared she'd shared too much? Maybe the topic had been too upsetting, or perhaps she'd gotten cold feet.

During an unrelated search for an old photograph, I found the last piece of shocking evidence that finished putting the picture together. On a separate drive labeled "Cesar" were duplicates of photos and texts I'd seen before, but one I didn't remember. It was a screenshot I'd taken of a travel itinerary. Cesar had flown Maria into the United States for a weekend visit. The dates caught me by surprise. She'd visited a few days after Cesar had asked me to marry him.

What if the entire relationship had been a con that they had conceived together?

Two weeks before I met Cesar online, he and Maria had taken a vacation. I found photos of them visiting famous sites. Shortly after this trip, his profile crossed my dating site feed, and our relationship began. During our first date, he admitted he'd been researching the topic of widows. I thought curiosity had prompted the search, but it was more likely an admission he'd targeted a particular group of women. Then he revealed surprise at finding me sexually attractive, confirming he wasn't looking for sex or love.

Cesar and Maria met after every important juncture or event: our official start of dating, our engagement, our wedding, and the brief 2018 split. A few months into the marriage, he wrote to her that he was miserable and trapped. I'd intercepted that letter and concluded Maria didn't know we'd gotten married, but she had known, which explains her odd reply. They stayed in touch like two conspirators plotting the next step.

In late 2017, I had made Cesar the heir to the Mexican company after learning of the country's onerous probate laws. Over the next two years, he urged aggressive investment in Mexican real estate. Once my inheritance had been spent on properties, he began to pressure me to do the same with my retirement fund.

As we used more of my net worth to grow the company, my health began to fail. I'd reoccurring bouts of clear watery diarrhea and worsening stomach pains. My urine had darkened and was frothy, my heart raced, joints ached, and white lines covered the width of my nail beds. I'd had two spells of unexplained vomiting and was admitted to the hospital with an unusually high white blood count with no signs of infection. Near the end of the marriage, I'd become pre-diabetic and showed the start of liver disease. Then I collapsed unconscious on the flight to Barbados. The onboard doctor was concerned I'd had suffered a mild heart attack or stroke. All these symptoms are consistent with poisoning.

A retired poison control specialist concurred. "Your symptoms fit a heavy metal poisoning profile, particularly arsenic," she said. "But it'd be difficult to prove since your last possible dosing was so long ago."

I now suspect Cesar married me for the money. Though I lack the hard evidence to prove it, he might have been spiking something, like my evening mineral water, to kill me.

Cesar is most likely a narcissistic sociopath who used camouflage and love-bombing to hide this condition. He mimicked some of my characteristics to build a fast rapport by creating a sense of twinship. On our first date, he gave me his copy of a book he said changed his life. He'd gift-wrapped the well-worn edition, marked with his favorite texts. Susan, the woman who had messaged me the last night of my honeymoon, wrote he'd given her the same book on their first date. At the beginning of our relationship, he'd start my day with a passage from the Bible. It never occurred to me that all of this might have been staged.

Susan thought she'd met someone who loved country music and animals. I thought I'd met an ambitious Christian man who liked classical music. It is doubtful either of those two personalities accurately describes Cesar. He had snared me by presenting who I wanted to see.

At the end of my marriage to Brad, I was a wreck. My entire adulthood had been spent in the service of others, from parents to partners to children. I'd learned at church to prioritize the needs of others. They'd taught that JOY meant J-Jesus came first, O-Others-second, and Y-You, (or me) last. I had defined myself in terms of another relationship—I was good as long as they were kept happy. Some form of emotional abuse had always permeated my life. Interpersonal boundaries were vague and shifted often.

A few days after my first date with Cesar, I fancied myself in love. Then, in a vulnerable moment, I shared too much. I told him I'd come into some money; worse yet—the exact amount. Such disclosures had been obligatory in the world I'd inhabited. Ashamed of what I'd done, I repressed the memory, only to recall it recently after watching a show about sexual addiction.

I'd been raised to believe God hates divorce, even when there are grounds. A godly woman stays married in support of her husband as a covenant she'd made with God. In my religious circles, women were urged to trust that God would change their wayward husband's hearts. Some churches routinely pass over divorced people for leadership positions, seeing it as a sign of failure.

My faith in God has been renewed but changed. Marriage is a mysterious union that symbolizes Christ's sacrificial love for the church, but I no longer believe it supersedes the value of a person's identity. God is like a roaring lion who fiercely protects me as his child and image-bearer. And, like a husband, he honors me with his selfless love. He has not called women to tolerate all forms of abuse as part of our religious duty.

While I threw myself into rescuing Cesar from his sexual addiction, he systematically manipulated me into quiet acquiescence. Psychological abuse changes the mind, creating confusion and doubt. Cesar used deception, misdirection, and emotional manipulation to hide his secret sexual life, then protected this carefully crafted reality with lies, gaslighting, and intimidation. His false persona was so convincing it fooled not only me but nearly everyone who met him, including friends and family. He tricked two polygraph tests and convinced three mental health professionals he was in recovery.

His abuse slowly eroded my belief in myself and my sense of reality. Research has shown sexual addiction induces trauma and injures both the partner and family across thirteen different psychological dimensions. I'd begun to distrust my decision-making skills, interpretation of the world, and gut. As my mental health deteriorated, I became more reliant on him. This allowed Cesar uninterrupted access to sexual acting out while gaining control over me and, ultimately, my money.

I must have appeared crazy as I swung between staying and leaving. For a long time, I tried to find evidence to resolve my ambivalence. I snooped through his stuff in the middle of the night and trailed him when he left the house. The problem was he was so adept at creating doubt I distrusted what I'd found. I failed to see *none of it mattered.* Instead of proving he was cheating, I should have based my decision on whether I felt safe, respected, and loved.

The horrible truth is Cesar most likely saw me as a means to a better life. In his digital files were home videos of his living situation about the time we'd met. He filmed a walk-through of his apartment. It was empty except for the bedroom, where a mattress had been thrown on the floor with a TV nearby. Clothes, still on hangers, littered the space. I now believe Cesar agreed to marry me to get the life he felt he deserved. He created a convincing reality of love and then used Maria's access to legal advice on Mexican law to trap me.

Besides the con, there's Cesar's sexual addiction.

Sexual intimacy is a vulnerable space when one person meets another. Sexual addiction, however, twists the pleasurable discovery of one another into the cannibalism of one by the other, with the sole purpose of satisfying the user's appetite.

Cesar used sex to dominate and control. He admitted it aroused him to violate or degrade another person. This explained his premature sexual advance on our first date, his requirement I go wigless on our second, and his continual struggles with sexual performance. He'd sought to compromise my integrity. And, once he'd accomplished that, our sex life quieted, except to appease me.

Betrayal trauma can happen to anyone. A person falls prey not because they are weak but because it is that *dangerous* and *insidious*. It slowly chips away at one's self-esteem until it's difficult to leave.

But there's one more part to this story—the saddest piece. Unprocessed traumatic events are stored in their raw form, waiting to be triggered. While swimming one afternoon, I was thinking through the book when suddenly I made the connection between my marriage and the abuse I suffered long ago.

On the nights my uncle spared me, he assaulted my younger sister. Those nights, I'd try to ignore the sounds of her cries. Yet her suffering left me wracked with guilt. Though I was only five years old, I blamed myself for failing to take her place and committed to doing better if I ever was faced with the same situation. Cesar and my sister share similar facial features, and both are younger children with histories of sexual assault. These similarities triggered my unconscious promise. Cesar's pleas for help then locked me in a terrible bind. Leaving him felt like abandoning her all over again, even though the situations bore little resemblance. I stayed too long in the deluded hopes I could change the ending of her story, even though it had already been written over forty years ago.

A nearly perfect set of circumstances had come together, and I was sunk. Trapped, I prayed for rescue. Cameron's illness offered me a way out—due to strong cultural traditions, Cesar had no choice but to allow me to leave the country. Once I'd discovered the con, he fled,

317

trying to recoup what he could, but Mexican law had cut my losses. Cesar's plans had backfired, and he ended up with less than an eighth of my estate.

I'm not a winner in this story, but thankfully, neither is he. In the two years since my divorce, I've discovered what genuinely makes me happy: I like who I am, and my life is what I make it.

APPENDIX

If you find yourself in a similar situation of emotional or physical abuse, or if you are in a relationship with sex addict, please reach out for support. Here are some helpful resources.

National Domestic Violence Hotline **1-800-799-7233**

National Sexual Assault Hotline **1-800-656-4673**

Sex Addiction and Recovery **1-440-951-5337**

Sex Addiction Anonymous **1-713-869-4902**

MORE ABOUT DR. MCAVOY

A GIFT FOR YOU

Have you left a toxic relationship?
Did you grow up in a dysfunctional home?

Dr. McAvoy has something for you!
Receive a year's worth of free weekly mental health tips sent right
to your inbox and begin the journey of rediscovering your enoughness.
https://mailchi.mp/kerrymcavoyphd/surviving-narcissism

AND BE SURE TO FOLLOW DR. MCAVOY

Instagram: @psychologistkerry
TikTok: @psychologistkerry
Visit her website at https://kerrymcavoyphd.com
Or contact her at hello@kerrymcavoyphd.com

Made in the USA
Middletown, DE
26 November 2022

16065143R00186